Familiar strangers...

Jennifer placed her hand lightly on her breasts, where the tiny butterfly fluttering seemed to have started. She and Chad had been much more intimate over the years than other people. They had never shared a physical intimacy, but that seemed almost superfluous compared to what they already had.

How could she say she didn't know the man sitting out there waiting so patiently for her? She knew him as well as she knew herself.

And she loved him with a depth of feeling that shook her with its intensity.

Jennifer opened the door and stepped out into the room.

Chad never took his eyes off her as he slowly came to his feet and walked over to her.

Jennifer went up on tiptoe and slid her arms around his neck. "Oh Chad, I love you so much," she whispered with trembling lips.

Dear Reader:

Welcome to Silhouette Desire – provocative, compelling, contemporary love stories written by and for today's woman. These are stories to treasure.

Each and every Silhouette Desire is a wonderful romance in which the emotional and the sensual go hand in hand. When you open a Desire, you enter a whole new world – a world that has, naturally, a perfect hero just waiting to whisk you away! A Silhouette Desire can be light-hearted or serious, but it will always be satisfying.

We hope you enjoy this Desire today – and will go on to enjoy many more.

Please write to us:

Jane Nicholls
Silhouette Books
PO Box 236
Thornton Road
Croydon
Surrey
CR9 3RU

Mystery Lover

ANNETTE BROADRICK

First published in Great Britain in 1994 by Silhouette Books, Eton House, 18-24 Paradise Road, Richmond, Surrey TW9 1SR

© Annette Broadrick 1987

Silhouette, Silhouette Desire and Colophon are Trade Marks of Harlequin Enterprises B.V.

ISBN 0 373 59385 6

22-9412

Made and printed in Great Britain

ANNETTE BROADRICK

believes in romance and the magic of life. Since 1984, when her first book was published, Annette has shared her view of life and love with readers all over the world.

Other Silhouette Books by Annette Broadrick

Silhouette Desire

Hunter's Prey
Bachelor Father
Hawk's Flight
Deceptions
Choices
Heat of the Night
Made in Heaven
Return to Yesterday
Adam's Story
Momentary Marriage
With All My Heart
A Touch of Spring
Irresistible
A Loving Spirit
Candlelight for Two
Lone Wolf
Where There Is Love
*Love Texas Style!
*Courtship Texas Style!
*Marriage Texas Style!
Zeke
Sound of Summer

Sons of Texas

*Silhouette Christmas
    Stories 1990*
"Christmas Magic"

Silhouette Special Edition

Mystery Wife

To Sherye Ritchie,
who creates a world of beauty wherever she goes....

Chapter One

Jennifer Chisholm opened her eyes in surprise and glanced around her living room. She must have fallen asleep while watching television. She couldn't decide what it was that had awakened her. Sam, her four-teen-pound tiger-striped cat, had made himself comfortable by draping himself across her as she lay on the couch. One outstretched paw rested softly against her cheek, the rest of him covered her to her knees. No wonder she'd slept so comfortably. She'd been sleeping under a fur coat—a living fur coat.

The low tones from the television drew her attention for a moment. The actors in a black-and-white movie, filmed more than fifty years ago, cavorted across the screen.

What time was it?

The rhythmic ticking of her clock was the only other sound in the room. She glanced to where it hung over her rolltop desk in the corner. The hands faithfully pointed out to her that it was ten minutes past two o'clock in the morning.

She had gratefully stretched out on the couch at nine in order to watch one of her favorite television shows before going to bed. Jennifer's day had been hectic. Her days were generally hectic when Mr. Cameron was out of the office. He'd been gone for almost a week now.

Jennifer was thankful that tomorrow was Saturday. She would have a couple of days to recuperate from her busy schedule. Hopefully he would be back in the office on Monday.

"I'm sorry, Sunshine. I'm afraid I miscalculated this one."

That was what had awakened her. Chad was contacting her. Jennifer's eyes widened. Her surprise wasn't due to the fact that she was suddenly hearing something when there was no one there—she was used to that. What had caught her off guard was that she hadn't heard from Chad since she'd told him off several months ago. There was only one person who referred to her as Sunshine—one person who didn't have to communicate with her by phone or in person.

When she was a small child she had referred to him as her invisible friend. The adults around her had been amused and a little sorry for her. An only child was often a lonely one. No doubt making up an invisible friend made life a little easier to handle.

Jennifer had never been able to convince anyone that she wasn't making him up. In time, she had stopped trying.

"Chad! What's wrong?" Her voice sounded loud in the room, but she hardly noticed. She could feel his agitation and pain, something she'd never felt with him before. Something was wrong—drastically wrong.

She tried to sit up, but Sam's weight on her chest seemed to hold her pressed against the sofa and cushions.

"Nothing that you can do anything about, I'm sorry to say. I just wanted you to know how very special you've been to me all these years."

Jennifer had never heard him pay her a compliment before. She had once told him that he only came into her life to bully and irritate her, and he'd never denied the accusation. Now he sounded so full of regret . . . as though he were telling her goodbye.

Once again she tried to sit up. Pushing against the sleeping cat, she said impatiently, "Would you get off me, darn it? You must weigh close to a ton!"

Jennifer felt a jolt as her remark reached Chad just before he said, *"I apologize for disturbing you at this hour. I should have realized. . . ."* He seemed to fade away.

"Don't leave, Chad!" she said rapidly. "I was talking to Sam."

"?"

"My cat. Don't you remember? I've had him for several years."

"I had forgotten the name."

"Please tell me what's wrong. You seem different, somehow." She stood up, concentrating on the voice in her head.

"That's not important. I just wanted to let you know, Sunshine, that I love you very much.... I always have."

Chad loved her? The irritating, teasing, invisible friend of her youth actually loved her? Jennifer couldn't believe what she was hearing.

"No, you're not dreaming."

That was a perfect example of why she found him so irritating. She found it most uncomfortable to have someone who could monitor—and offer unasked-for comments on—her thoughts. But Jennifer had to admit that the past few months had been very lonely without him.

He'd been such an integral part of her life for so long that she hadn't realized how much she would miss his presence. If she'd known, she would never have yelled at him, ordered him to get out of her life and to leave her alone.

He had done just that.

Now he was back and she knew something was seriously wrong.

"What is it?"

"I didn't mean to upset you. I just needed to—"

"I'm going to be much more than just upset if you don't tell me what's wrong."

"I walked into a trap, I'm afraid. Well laid, I might add. They knew me well enough to know my curiosity would keep me following them until they had me."

"Will you kindly tell me what you're talking about?"

"It's too late to go into it. It's never been important for you to know what I do for a living. It's not important now. I just wanted to tell you I love you and

hope life showers you with the blessings you deserve.''

''Chad, please tell me what's wrong.'' She waited for a moment but got no response. ''Chad?'' There was no answer.

Frustrated beyond belief, Jennifer sank down beside Sam once more and stared unseeingly at the television.

How could he do this to her: check in to say goodbye and then leave again?

If she could just once get her hands on him she'd—

But that was the trouble. She had never laid eyes on him.

Dropping her head wearily on the back of the sofa, Jennifer tried to clear her mind. Chad had a way of getting her emotions stirred up. He was good at that. He always had been....

Jennifer couldn't remember exactly how old she was when Chad had first made his presence known, but she knew it was some time after the automobile accident that had changed her life. Her mother, upon being questioned, had said Jennifer was just past five years of age when the accident had occurred. Jennifer remembered very little about it and often wondered if what she knew was what she had remembered or what others had told her later.

After several days in the hospital following the accident, her father had died, leaving her mother to find a way to support herself and Jennifer.

No one was to blame for the fact that Jennifer had trouble making friends. She was shy and often stood on the sidelines and waited for someone to include her in their games.

As she grew older, and her mother allowed her to go home alone after school, she returned to an empty apartment where she waited for her mother to get off work.

Jennifer had grown increasingly despondent in the months following the accident. Until Chad spoke to her one day....

Jennifer had stood looking out the window of their Oceanside, California apartment, yearning for the days when her mother had been home and would take her to the beach. Jennifer loved to play on the beach and to watch the waves as they came rolling in to touch the shoreline.

Now her mother had so little time for her. Jennifer had no one anymore.

"You have me, Sunshine."

Jennifer glanced around the room. There was no one there. She glanced at the television but it wasn't on.

"Who said that?" she finally asked softly.

"I did."

"Who are you?"

There was a brief pause before she heard, *"Chad."*

Jennifer started walking through the apartment, looking behind doors, vaguely aware that although she was hearing someone, the messages seemed to come from inside her head.

"They are," he confirmed. *"I'm sending you thought messages."*

"Do I know you?" she finally asked, puzzled.

"It's enough that I know you, Sunshine. I just wanted you to know that I'm here. You don't have to feel lonely."

"Are you real?"

- *"Real enough."*

"I mean, you aren't my guardian angel, are you?"

She could feel his amusement. *"Something like that, maybe. But I'm very much a human being."*

"How old are you?"

"Oh, I'm very old. Almost ancient."

Jennifer didn't doubt that at all. How many people could talk to you in your head? She'd never known of anyone who did that before.

She asked her mother about Chad when she got home. Unfortunately her mother had too much on her mind to really tune in to Jennifer's questions and absently replied that she supposed everyone had a guardian angel, and she was pleased to know that Jennifer's angel went by the name of Chad.

Of course her schoolmates made fun of her. Jennifer discovered that she didn't care. Probably they were so busy they didn't even hear their angels talking to them.

She could always hear Chad.

But by the time Jennifer reached her teenage years, she discovered that Chad was far from being an angel.

"Why are you mooning over that picture of a movie star?" he asked one day.

Jennifer glanced around, embarrassed to be caught gazing with longing at her idol's photograph. Then she realized she hadn't been caught. It was Chad.

"I'm not mooning."

"Of course you are. Why do you think someone like him would never notice you? You have a very nice figure."

"I'm skinny."

"No, you're not. And stop worrying about the size of your breasts. They're just fine."

"Chad!"

"Did I say something wrong?"

"I just wish I could see you as clearly as you seem to see me."

"You probably could, if you concentrated. All it takes is practice."

She had taken him at his word. Jennifer never managed to pick up anything to do with his appearance, but she had learned to contact him whenever she wished, which proved to be a little unsettling for him on one occasion.

"Chad! Mother said I can't go with Sue and Janey to the show tonight. You know that isn't fair. What can I tell her to convince her I won't get into any trouble if she'd just let me go?"

She waited for a few moments, but didn't get an answer.

"Chad?"

"Not now, Jennifer. I'm busy."

He'd never been too busy for her before. They'd been conversing for years now. He'd helped her with her homework, explained algebra to her so that she finally understood it. Why, Chad had always been there for her.

"Busy? Doing what?"

What she received then was something akin to a groan. *"Thanks a lot, Sunshine. You just blew that one for me!"*

"What did I do?"

"My dear, sweet, innocent child. There are times when my mind is on other things and I don't need the distraction."

"Are you with a girl?" she asked suspiciously.

"I was. I'm afraid my lack of concentration at a crucial moment offended her."

"Oh, Chad. I'm sorry."

"Believe me. No sorrier than I am."

She didn't know what to say. Jennifer had forgotten why she had flounced into her room. The idea that Chad had a life totally unrelated to hers had never occurred to her before. She had always taken him so much for granted.

Several days passed before she attempted to contact him again.

"Chad?"

"Yes?"

"Are you busy?"

"What's up, Sunshine?"

"Oh . . . nothing much. I was just wondering about something. . . ."

"Uh-oh. Now you're curious. I was afraid of that."

"Would it be possible for us to meet sometime?"

"Possible, but not practical."

"Why not?"

"Because I don't live in Oceanside."

"Oh!" She had never given his residence any thought either. "Where do you live?"

"Why do you ask?"

"Because I'd like to get to know you better."

"What do you want to know?" Before she could say anything she felt his laughter. *"Whoa, whoa. Wait a minute. Some of those questions are indecent. And no. I don't look anything like your favorite television hero."*

"How old are you?"

"Much too old for a little girl like you."

"Are you married?"

"No."

"Do you intend to get married?"

"Maybe."

"When?"

"Maybe I'm waiting for you to grow up."

"What good will that do, if I don't know who you are?"

"Ah, but I know who you are and that's what counts."

"You mean you've actually seen me?"

"Of course."

"When?"

"Whenever I come to Oceanside."

"Where are you now?"

There was a hesitation. *"I travel around considerably. Part of my job."*

"What's your job?"

"If I thought you needed to know, Sunshine, I'd tell you."

"You can be so irritating. Did you know that?"

"Now that you mention it, you aren't the first person who's pointed out that trait to me. Perhaps I should work on it."

"Perhaps, nothing." Jennifer was walking home from school and realized that more than one person passing her had given her a strange look. She supposed she did look a little peculiar, walking down the street arguing with someone who obviously wasn't there. "Are you serious about waiting for me to grow up?"

There was a long pause and she thought he wasn't going to answer her. *"No. I'm not serious, Sunshine. I guess I was just trying to be irritating, as usual. My life-style isn't conducive to a marriage arrangement, I'm afraid."*

"Oh." Jennifer could feel the depression settling through her.

"But I'll always be here for you, no matter what. Don't forget that."

"How will I ever explain you to my husband?" she said, attempting to convey a lightness she didn't feel.

"You won't have to. I would never intrude when you didn't need me. Once you're married, things will be different."

"I don't want to lose you, Chad."

Jennifer could still hear herself repeating those words. Even when she'd gotten so angry at him, she hadn't really meant for him to take her so literally and to drop out of her life.

Chad was special. They had a very special relationship.

Now he was in some sort of trouble. If only she could figure out something she could do to help him. She'd do anything.

"Anything?"

"Chad! You're still there! Yes. Tell me what to do."

"I've been thinking...."

"Yes?"

"You are my only contact with the world right now. My abductors figured all the angles but that one."

"Your abductors! You mean you've been kidnapped?"

"More or less. They aren't holding me for ransom, though. They just don't intend for me to show up again."

"Could I call the police or something?"

"I'm working on that. Why don't you get some sleep while I think through my plan a little more thoroughly. Let me know when you wake up. Surely there's some way we can utilize our special communication."

She laughed. "I'd love to. You've done so much for me. Now it's my turn."

"We aren't playing games here, Sunshine. These people mean business. I really walked into a hornet's nest with this one. Now, go get some sleep."

Jennifer checked the door to be sure the chain was on and the lock secure, turned off the television and snapped off the lights. He was right. She would have to get some rest. If Chad felt he could wait until morning, then she'd try to get a few more hours of sleep.

She had a hard time quieting down her mind once she crawled into bed with Sam curled up behind her drawn-up knees. After all these years, she now had the chance to meet Chad in person.

Chapter Two

By nine o'clock the next morning Jennifer was driving her five-year-old Toyota toward Las Vegas.

For the past five years Jennifer had been living and working in the Los Angeles area. She was pleased with her job, her apartment and her life-style. To be more precise, she was content to stay in the shallows of life, never tempted to seek out the depths and excitement that others seemed to crave. Chad had a lot to do with her way of thinking. He had spent many hours talking to her about some of the trouble young women could get into if they weren't careful, especially if they were trying to prove something, to either themselves or other people.

Jennifer realized she didn't have such a need. She was content to be who she was and live her own rather unexciting life.

Therefore, this would be her first visit to Las Vegas.

Jennifer wasn't particularly looking forward to arriving there. Her attitude could be traced back to the fact that Chad had been less than forthcoming about what he wanted her to do.

Following his instructions, she had immediately hopped into the shower as soon as she awakened, quickly donned her clothes, then contacted him.

He immediately responded.

"How are you?" she asked, more out of concern than politeness.

"I feel a little groggy, but that's to be expected," was the reply.

"Have you been drinking?" she asked, surprised.

"No. But I got a fairly hard clout to the head last night."

"Oh."

"They've made it clear that I have offended their sensibilities by being so nosy. They have a very physical way of showing their displeasure."

"Who are 'they'?"

"I can't give you a positive ID at the moment, Sunshine. Are you still willing to help me?"

"Oh, of course. What do you want me to do?"

"Go to Las Vegas."

"Las Vegas? What are you doing there?"

"I'm not in Las Vegas. I want you to contact a man there for me. You'll have to see him in person and he's tough to reach. I would say almost impossible, as a matter of fact. But you've got to try. He's the only one who might have an idea how to find me."

"Who is he?"

"His name is Tony Carillo. He owns the Lucky Lady Casino."

Jennifer could feel her heart leap in her chest. "You want me to go find a gambler?"

"I'm not concerned with his personal habits at the moment, Sunshine. He's the one who can help me."

"What do you want me to tell him?"

"Wait until you get to Vegas and I'll tell you."

"Chad! Must you be so mysterious?"

"At this point, yes. You don't have to do this if you don't want to."

"I didn't say that. Of course I'll go."

Jennifer found a small bag and gathered a few of her clothes and cosmetics. No doubt she'd be gone the entire weekend.

The day was going to be another hot one, Jennifer decided soon after she left the apartment. But then, what could you expect in August? If she'd ever thought about going to Las Vegas, which she hadn't, she was sure she would have picked a cooler time of the year.

Jennifer could not get rid of the tight knot of excitement that seemed to have formed in her chest. At long last she was going to find out more about Chad.

He had reluctantly told her that Tony was an old friend of his and if anyone could get him out of his present precarious situation, Tony could.

What Jennifer also realized was that Tony could tell her a great deal about Chad that she had always wanted to know.

Jennifer faced the fact that rushing to Las Vegas to help Chad was the most exciting thing that had ever happened to her—which certainly seemed to make a statement about her life.

Actually, having Chad in her life was the only exciting thing that had ever happened to her. After a very careful poll among her classmates while she was growing up, Jennifer had discovered that she seemed to be the only person blessed with an invisible friend.

She had quickly learned not to discuss him with anyone, and what else, after all, did she have to talk about? Jennifer hadn't been interested in dating because she never knew what to say. She didn't care anything about cars and that was what most of the boys talked about.

So she had spent many hours talking to Chad about things she was interested in, things she had read about in books, or magazines. She had known he was much older than she was and had a great deal more experience with life. Yet he had always been very patient with her, willing to discuss any subject she brought up.

Jennifer smiled to herself, remembering how he had dealt with her questions about sex. Now that she thought about it, those questions should have been asked of her mother, but whenever she broached the subject, her mother had seemed embarrassed and Jennifer had allowed her curiosity about the subject to drop.

Chad had been much more matter-of-fact. She had been lying there in bed one night, thinking about some of the stories she was hearing at school, when Chad had spoken up.

"Don't believe everything you hear, Sunshine. It could get you into trouble."

"If you think that I would do something like that—" she started to say indignantly, when he interrupted.

"Of course you will...at the right time and with the right person. But sex isn't something to be experimented with, like a toy. The act of love is all tied up with our emotions. When it's used only as a tool to convince people around us that we're adults, we can get hurt and hurt many others as well."

They had talked long into the night, and by the time Jennifer fell asleep she felt as though she had graduated from childhood.

His lessons had stuck with her through the years. Although she had dated once she moved to Los Angeles and began working, she had never been tempted to prove anything with anyone. Nor had she met anyone with whom she wished to share such intimacy.

Perhaps she wasn't the type to marry. She certainly didn't draw second looks in a crowd. Jennifer had always been disgusted that she'd stopped growing when she was only a couple of inches over five feet. Although she had often been told that her eyes were her most striking feature, whenever she looked into the mirror all she could see were wide blue eyes staring back. Even her hair wasn't a real color. She wasn't quite a blonde, nor was her hair dark enough to be considered brown. Jennifer thought of herself as an almost person. Almost average height, but not quite, almost blond, but not quite, almost attractive...but not quite.

Not that it mattered to her, she reminded herself firmly. She was content with her life. And now, she was doing something for Chad that would help to repay all the wonderful things he had done for her through the years. She smiled at the thought.

Eventually her mind made its way to her job, and for the first time, she felt a little uneasy. Jennifer hadn't given a thought to whether she would be back home in time to go to work on Monday. If not, she wondered what she should do.

Jennifer had taken a secretarial course as soon as she completed high school. It had been important to her that she be independent as soon as possible. Her mother's health had never been good and Jennifer wanted to relieve her of the burden.

She could have stayed in Oceanside but preferred to get away, to make new friends, to experience new things. Her new life would have been very lonely if she hadn't had Chad.

Surprisingly enough, Jennifer made many friends at the school, and when one of them mentioned that the Cameron Investigation Service was looking for stenographers, she and two of the other graduates had applied.

Jennifer had been surprised at the size of the place. She wasn't sure what she had expected, but certainly nothing on the scale that met her eyes. The receptionist sent her to the personnel director, who tested her and had her fill out the necessary applications. The director explained that Mr. Cameron managed to keep several stenographers busy transcribing the reports he dictated.

C. W. Cameron had built quite a reputation, so Jennifer was told, as an insurance investigator. Although he was out in the field quite often, he kept in touch with the office and oftentimes called in and dictated on the machines that were set up to take telephone transcriptions.

Jennifer had been working there for almost five years and she thoroughly enjoyed her job. She had been Mr. Cameron's administrative assistant for several years now, handling as much as possible for him when he was out of the office, doing the preliminary investigations of cases—the tedious, time-consuming research that went with that sort of investigation—then turning them over to him to follow up the leads she uncovered.

They worked well together and he paid her quite well. Jennifer felt it was unfortunate that Mr. Cameron was such a cold, unfeeling individual. Perhaps it came with the job, or something.

After all the years she had worked for him, he still insisted on calling her Ms. Chisholm. In this day and age of immediate first names and instant friendships, C. W. Cameron was a throwback to another era.

He wasn't all that old, either. Jennifer had gotten a glimpse of his insurance file once, which stated his age as thirty-seven. He didn't look that old, until you gazed into his eyes. His eyes seemed to have too much knowledge about people and their behavior.

Some of the women in the office teased her about working for him, since he was single and more than a little handsome, with his tawny-colored hair and sherry-colored eyes. Jennifer shivered a little. He might be attractive, but he was too cold a person to ever attract her.

Jerry was more her type. She had been dating him occasionally for almost a year now. She really enjoyed Jerry. He was relaxed, easygoing, fun-loving, and did not pressure her to deepen their relationship. Too bad she couldn't combine the personality of the one man with the brilliant mind and incisive intellect of the other one. What a combination that would be.

Jennifer suddenly remembered that she had a date that night with Jerry, and she had totally forgotten about it. He would be over to pick her up and she wouldn't be there. How could she have been so absentminded? When Chad had contacted her, everything else had flown out the window.

She would have to call him and explain as soon as she got to Vegas. Explain what? Jennifer had never been able to find the words to tell Jerry about Chad. At first, it hadn't been important. They had been casual friends, neighbors until Jerry had moved to be closer to his new job. Occasionally he would have her over to eat popcorn and watch television. Once in a while she would prepare a meal for them and they'd go see a movie. After he moved, they spent less time together, but he still called to see how she was doing and to talk about his job.

Jennifer had never stood him up before. Surely he would understand that something unexpected had come up that changed her plans.

By the time she reached the outskirts of Las Vegas, Jennifer was tired and hungry. She hadn't wanted to stop and eat, which was a good thing. Crossing the desert hadn't given her much opportunity.

First things first. She would find a restaurant, eat and call Jerry.

He answered on the fourth ring.

"Am I interrupting anything?" she asked.

"Oh, hi, Jennie. I must have fallen asleep. Couldn't figure out what was happening at first."

"Things must be tough on the job these days, huh?"

He laughed. "No. Just resting up for our big date tonight."

"That's why I called, Jerry. I'm afraid I'm going to have to cancel."

"Is there something wrong?" She heard the concern in his voice.

"Not really. A friend needed some help this weekend and I volunteered."

"Where are you? I keep getting all kinds of background noises."

"I'm in a restaurant."

"Oh. Well, I'm sorry I won't see you tonight. I've been saving all kinds of things to tell you."

"Look, why don't I call you next week? We can check our schedules and pick another time, okay?"

"Sure. No problem. Well, you take care. I'll talk to you later."

Jennifer hung up and walked out to her car. The desert heat caused her to wish she'd worn something besides her jeans and shirt. One of her halter tops and a pair of shorts would have been more appropriate.

"Not in a casino, Sunshine."

"Oh! There you are. You pop up at the most unexpected times."

"I told you I'd contact you once you got to Vegas, didn't I?"

She shrugged and realized that that wasn't much of an answer. "Okay. I'm here now. What next?"

"I want you to go into the Lucky Lady Casino, go all the way to the back. You'll see a sign that says Manager's Office. Whoever is there, tell them that you need to see Tony Carillo. That you have a message from Tiger and that you have to see him personally to deliver it."

"Tiger?"

"That's right."

"And he'll know what I mean?"

"Sunshine, this isn't going to work if you're going to question and analyze everything I tell you to do. Are you with me or not?"

"Of course I'm with you. I wouldn't be here if I wasn't."

"No need to get testy. All right. The Lucky Lady is on the Strip. You shouldn't have any trouble finding it."

She didn't.

Now that the time had come for her to do something, Jennifer felt her heart begin to race in her chest. She had never before realized what a coward she was. There seemed to be no adventure in her soul. No doubt there were many people who would enjoy the mystery and intrigue of what she was now doing. But not her.

"You can back out anytime."

"Oh, shut up," she muttered. A couple coming out of the casino glared at her as they passed. "I'm sorry, I wasn't talking to you," she tried to explain. They pointedly looked around the area. No one else was around. Jennifer knew her smile was a little weak as she shrugged and hurried on in.

"I thought I taught you better manners, Sunshine."

She kept her head down and tried not to move her lips. "This is not the time to go into my behavior, Chad. I'm doing the best I can at the moment. I'm just not used to this sort of thing."

"That's what I've been trying to tell you. You've limited yourself too much all these years. You need to reach out and stretch your potential to its maximum."

"Right now all I want to do is find Tony Carillo."

"May I help you?" The beautiful young woman sitting at the desk in the manager's office asked Jennifer a few moments later.

"Yes. I'd like to see Mr. Carillo."

"Do you have an appointment, Ms.—"

"Chisholm. Jennifer Chisholm. Uh, no. I'm afraid not. Would you tell him that I have a message for him from—uh, er—Tiger?"

"Tiger?"

Jennifer could feel the heat in her cheeks as she determinedly kept her gaze on the woman in front of her. "That's correct. I'm supposed to deliver it in person."

The woman picked up the phone on the desk and dialed. Then she spoke quietly into the receiver. She waited, obviously listening to something, then responded and hung up the phone.

Her gaze was filled with speculation when she glanced back at Jennifer. "There's an elevator across the lobby. Push the top button. Someone will meet you to show you his office."

"Good work, Sunshine. You passed the first hurdle."

"What do I do next?"

"Wait until you meet Tony, then I'll tell you."

"What's the matter, don't you trust me?"

"Yes. I just want to make sure they aren't giving you the runaround."

Jennifer stepped off the elevator onto plush carpeting. A young man about her age stood there waiting. He grinned. "You're here to see Tony, right?"

She nodded her head.

"This way."

She followed the man down the hallway and into a well-decorated office. A secretarial desk was on one side, and what looked like a word processing unit was carefully covered. There was nobody in the office.

The young man tapped on another door, then opened it. Motioning for her to enter first, he waited until she passed him, then quietly closed the door behind her. She was now alone with the man Chad called Tony Carillo.

His office appeared to be the size of Jennifer's entire apartment. She looked at the ornate wall hangings and furnishings with awe before her eyes turned to the man who had gotten up from behind a massive desk and started toward her.

He looked to be in his mid-thirties, and was of medium height, with dark hair and eyes. He held out his hand to her as he approached.

"I'm afraid I wasn't told your name, young lady," he said with the hint of a smile. "The only information I got was that you have a message from Tiger."

"Jennifer. Jennifer Chisholm. I was told to—"

"Ahh. So you are Chad's Jennifer." He took her hand and held it between both of his. "Yes. He has chosen well."

"Chosen?"

"What I meant to say was that I've heard many things about you and am delighted to meet you at last."

"You know Chad well?"

He laughed. "Extremely well. We grew up together in California."

"Oh."

"So what can I do for you? You said you had a message from him."

"From Tiger."

"Right."

"You mean Chad and Tiger are the same person?"

"Yeah. It was a joke because we always hung around together. You know...Tony—the Tiger." His smile widened. "That was probably before your time."

"He's in trouble."

Tony's smile disappeared. He led her to a sofa and they sat down. "What sort of trouble?" he asked with a frown.

"I'm not sure. He said he walked into a trap."

Tony gazed out the window and she could tell that he was thinking. Finally he turned back to her. "Where is he?"

"He didn't say."

"When was the last time you talked with him?"

"Well, you see—"

"Tell him late last night."

"Late last night," she managed to parrot.

"Uh-oh. Then something must have turned sour at the last minute. He thought he had them for sure."

"You talked to him recently?"

"Yes. He's working on something for me."

Jennifer gave a quick sigh of relief. "Oh, good. Then you can help him."

"Not if I don't know where he is. I know who he was dealing with, though. Max can play rough."

Jennifer wished she knew what more to say. Never had she felt more helpless.

"Tell him that I'm somewhere in southern Utah, in the mountains. I'm in some sort of shack. I haven't seen anyone since they dumped me here last night. I have a hunch no one is going to bother to see if I'm eating. There's nothing here."

Jennifer repeated Chad's words. When she finished, Tony stared at her in confusion. "I thought you just said you didn't know where he was."

"Well, I didn't. I still don't. That isn't enough information to find him, is it?"

"It's a hell of a start, let me tell you. Max, the man I've been hoping to get enough evidence on to take to court, owns property in southern Utah. Before we had this falling out, he took me up there hunting a couple of times. I think I know exactly where that shack is."

"That's a relief, Sunshine. Looks like you've managed to get me some help."

"May I go with you to find him?" she asked.

"No!" Chad replied quickly.

"I can't see any reason why not. I'm sure you're anxious about him."

If he only knew. After all this time she was finally going to meet Chad face-to-face.

Chapter Three

Sunshine, I don't want you involved in this. Let Tony do what he has to do. You go on back to L.A."

Tony had left his office, telling her to wait while he made some arrangements, so Jennifer was alone.

"Chad, I want to know that you're all right."

"I will be. Just as soon as Tony gets here."

"I want to help."

"You already have. Now go home."

"No."

After a moment of silence, he replied. *"Sunshine, I know that you want to see me. Believe me, it isn't necessary to our relationship."*

"Maybe not as far as you're concerned."

"Didn't you tell me you no longer wanted me in your life?"

"I was angry at the time."

"But you were right. I was trying to run interference for you, trying to make your life easier for you. No one can do that for someone else. I need to keep my distance and allow you to live your own life."

"And make my own mistakes."

"Exactly."

"If you hadn't warned me, I would have made a very bad one."

"And by warning you, I almost destroyed our relationship."

"You could never do that. I just overreacted."

She had been been at work one afternoon when her boss had returned from lunch with one of his clients.

"Ms. Chisholm," C. W. Cameron said, pausing in front of her desk, "I'd like you to meet Larry Donahue. Larry, my assistant, Jennifer Chisholm."

For a moment Jennifer could only stare at the man who held out his hand. He could be the very same man whose photograph had hung on her wall when she was a teenager—her movie idol. The same flashing smile, shining blue eyes, the same rumpled black curls falling across his forehead.

"Jennifer, did he say? I'm so pleased to meet you. C. W. tells me you're invaluable to him."

Her eyes quickly met the unsmiling gaze of her employer. He had said that about her? Mr. Cameron was a man of few words, and those were seldom complimentary. Of course he had always been prompt with her raises and Christmas bonuses, so he must be pleased with her work. She smiled at the incredibly sexy man in front of her. "I enjoy my job, Mr. Donahue." She glanced at her boss, then turned her gaze to the man standing beside him. "I'm happy to hear that Mr. Cameron is pleased with my work." Her employer's expression didn't change. He nodded his head in acknowledgment of her words and waited for his client.

"I'd enjoy seeing you again, Jennifer. Would you be interested in having dinner with me tonight?"

Jennifer was taken aback by the blunt approach of the man in front of her. "Oh! Well, I, uh—" She glanced at her boss but could not read anything in his expression. Meeting the pleading gaze of the other man, she smiled and replied softly, "I'd like that."

Larry's grin caused a quiver to run through her. "Great. Why don't I pick you up when you get off work? We can go from here."

"I'm not sure when I'll be through tonight and I'd much prefer to go home and freshen up first."

Larry shrugged. "No problem. Let me have your address. I'll pick you up, say, around seven-thirty, if that's all right?"

She smiled and nodded, delighted with the man and his obvious eagerness to get to know her better. After writing down her address, she gave it to him.

Larry turned to the man beside him and stuck out his hand. "I really enjoyed our meeting, C. W. I'm sure if anyone can get to the bottom of this mess, you will."

Jennifer watched C. W. Cameron give Larry one of his rare smiles. "I appreciate your confidence. I'll be in touch with you in a few days."

"Fine." He left the office, giving Jennifer a quick salute that she found enchanting.

"You've made a conquest," her boss said quietly.

She searched his face for some clue as to what he was thinking.

"Do you mind that I agreed to go out with him?"

He raised his brows and shook his head. "What you do on your own time is none of my business." He glanced down at the stack of mail in front of her. "Is there anything there I need to see this afternoon?"

"Oh, yes, there's a couple of things I wanted to check with you—"

He turned away. "Bring them in," he said, striding through the door to his office.

She picked up the stack of mail and shook her head. She had never known anyone to be as distant with people as her employer. They had known each other for several years and yet they had nothing but the business in common. It was just as well, she supposed. He was a fair employer, treated her well. What more could she ask?

A little warmth, maybe? A little personal interest? Something more than his usual "good morning," or "I'll be back later," or "I'll be out of town for a while." She wondered if he ever really saw her as a person, or whether he thought that she had arrived along with the rest of the office equipment—with a serial number tattooed somewhere on her body.

What difference did it make? She had a date that night with a man that had stepped out of her dreams. This could be the beginning of a beautiful relationship. Jennifer smiled as she followed her boss into his office.

She was singing as she got out of the shower that night.

"What's put you in such a good mood, Sunshine?"

"Oh, hi, Chad." There were times when she was definitely glad that he couldn't see her, especially now, when she was drying off from the shower. There was something to be said for their type of communication. "I have a date tonight."

"I've never known you to be this excited about seeing Jerry."

She laughed. "You're right. I met someone new today. His name is Larry Donahue."

"Are you talking about the real estate developer?"

"I don't know. He's hired Mr. Cameron to do some investigative work for him."

"You have no business going out with Larry Donahue."

Slowly Jennifer straightened from drying her legs. She reached over and pulled her robe off the hook from behind the door. Sliding her arms into the sleeves, she carefully tied the sash before saying anything. Somehow she felt more prepared to do battle when she wasn't bare.

"I know that you're concerned about me, Chad, and I appreciate that. However, I'm a big girl now. I can pick and choose my own dates."

"Come on, Sunshine, don't be that way. I didn't mean to offend you. But that man is a womanizer. Besides making money, his biggest ambition in life is to see how many women he can coax into bed with him."

"How can you say that about someone you don't even know?"

"Because I do know him. In addition, I know his type."

"Well, he seemed very nice to me and I agreed to go out with him. I'm certainly not going to greet him at the door with the news that my invisible friend has forbidden me to go out with him."

"Just be careful, will you please? For my sake?"

"What do you mean, for your sake? What business is it of yours?"

"Remember when you used to call me your guardian angel?"

"That was many long years ago, before I discovered you were far from being an angel!"

"You allowed me to protect you then, Sunshine. Don't push me away now."

Jennifer began to blow-dry her hair, effectively drowning out anything Chad might try to say. When it was dry, she quickly put on her makeup, touched up her hair with the curling iron and went into the bedroom.

Larry would be there soon and she still hadn't decided what to wear.

"Nothing too enticing."

"Chad, I don't even have anything enticing! Would you leave me alone?"

"Just be careful that you don't give him the wrong impression about you."

"Fine. I could have worn my nun habit if I hadn't just sent it to the cleaners."

"Very funny."

"You're being ridiculous, Chad. You're worse than a father."

"I know. That's what I've tried to be—the father you lost, the older brother you never had...."

Jennifer felt ashamed of herself. "Chad, you have been everything I've ever wanted in a best friend, and believe me, I appreciate all that you've done. But I'm a big girl now. You've got to let me grow up."

"I know you're a big girl now. Why else do you suppose Larry Donahue is interested in you?"

She found one of her favorite dresses, made in a soft peach color, and quickly slid it over her head. It had long full sleeves, a scooped neckline, and from a fitted waist flowed into a full skirt that ended mid-calf.

"All right, Chad. Are you satisfied? This dress would fit in very well at a PTA meeting."

The doorbell rang and she hurried to the door without waiting for a response.

Her evening with Larry Donahue turned out to be delightful. He treated Jennifer like a princess. She realized midway through the evening that Chad's warnings had made her nervous and at first she'd been a little tense. However, Larry could not have treated her with more kindness and consideration. After dinner they went to two different clubs to dance, and by the time he took her back home Jennifer felt as though she were floating several inches off the ground.

Of course she invited him in. That was the only polite thing to do. After making coffee they sat and chatted on her sofa. Knowing that Sam might annoy him, she had even had the foresight to put the cat in her bedroom and close the door.

Larry had made several suggestions during the evening of other things they might enjoy doing together, so she knew he planned to see her again. Jennifer could see nothing wrong when he leaned over and kissed her. He wasn't pushy, nor did he make her feel this was the first step to a well-planned seduction. It was a get-acquainted sort of kiss and Jennifer responded appropriately.

"Don't forget what I told you, Sunshine. Be careful."

Jennifer's mind suddenly snapped back into awareness from the floating bliss Larry's kiss had provided. How dare Chad interrupt her at this point in the evening! He'd never done anything like it before.

She forced herself to concentrate on the words, *Go away, Chad.* He was always so good at reading her thoughts. Surely he'd get that message.

Larry must have felt her stiffen in his arms because he drew back slightly.

"I've enjoyed this evening so much, Jennifer. Thank you for spending it with me."

"I've enjoyed myself very much, Larry."

"I don't want to overstay my welcome," he said with a charming smile. "May I call you?"

"Of course."

She walked him to the door. He stood there looking down at her for a moment. "You are so beautiful. I can't understand how you've managed to stay single."

Jennifer laughed. He sounded sincere enough, but since she looked in the mirror every day, she knew what she looked like. Perhaps he did have a way of exaggerating things.

Larry slowly pulled her into his arms and kissed her. She relaxed against him.

"Has he mentioned his wife and three children yet?"

Jennifer's eyes flew open and she gasped. That was a low blow. Even Chad couldn't stoop to such a thing.

"What's wrong?" Larry asked, puzzled when she jerked away from him.

"Do you have a wife and three children?" she blurted out suddenly.

He looked a little taken aback at the timing of her question. "As a matter of fact, I do, but I'm not sure why you should bring them up at this time."

She stared at him in disbelief. The same charming smile, the flashing eyes, the black curls tumbling across his forehead. He didn't even seem concerned that she had asked. For a moment, too many thoughts were racing through her head for her to say a thing.

"I wasn't trying to keep them a secret or anything. I assumed that C. W. told you I was married."

"No, he didn't."

"Oh. I take it that makes a difference to you."

"It certainly does. I'm sure that it makes a difference to your wife, too."

"My wife and I understand each other very well. There's no problem where she's concerned."

"Well, I'm very much afraid that there's a problem where I'm concerned." She opened the door. "Good night, Mr. Donahue."

He shook his head, puzzled at the abrupt change in her behavior, and walked out the door.

After carefully closing the door behind him, she slumped against it. What a letdown to what had been a beautiful evening.

"He was right, you know. You really are a beautiful woman—inside and out, Sunshine."

Jennifer straightened and wished that Chad was standing in front of her. She would dearly have loved to throw something at him.

"Why would you want to throw something at me? What did I do?"

"As if you didn't know. You ruined a beautiful evening for me."

"How could I ruin it?"

"You know very well what you did. Every time he kissed me, you made some sort of a comment."

"Oh, did I? How rude of me. I'm really very sorry."

"Sure you are. You knew exactly what you were doing!"

"Well, not exactly. But whenever your thoughts go a little hazy and syrupy I know something is going on."

Jennifer stormed into her bedroom and was greeted by Sam, who protested his recent incarceration.

"And I don't want to hear anything from you, either!" she exclaimed, reaching around and unzipping her dress. When Sam continued to bemoan her unfair treatment of him she eventually sat down on the bed and scooped him up in her lap, stroking his long coat and wishing she could think of something to put Chad in his place.

"Hey, Sunshine, I really am sorry if I upset you. That wasn't what I meant to do."

"Wasn't it? It seems to me that ever since I first met you, you've been telling me what to do, how to do it, when to do it and what not to do. Frankly, I'm sick of it."

There was no response.

"And that's another thing. There's no way I can argue with you. Whenever I try you just clam up and disappear and I can't reach you."

"You always reach me, Sunshine. Sometimes I just don't choose to answer."

"That's what I mean. I can't argue with myself."

"Good point. Think about it."

Jumping to her feet, Jennifer dropped Sam on the bed. "I am sick of you, do you understand that? I wish you would just go away and leave me alone!"

"Do you really mean that?"

"I wouldn't have said it if I didn't mean it." She waited for a reply but there was nothing more. After a few minutes she said, "Chad?" There was no answer.

So he had taken her at her word. She was glad. She wasn't a child anymore and didn't need a guardian angel or whoever he thought he was being.

Now Jennifer stood in Tony's office, looking out the window. Chad had never contacted her again. Not until last night. She had missed him. Missed his sense of humor, his teasing and tantalizing, missed his caring about what happened to her.

Now she had a chance to meet him and she wasn't going to let the opportunity slip by. She grinned at the thought. He was obviously a captive. There was nothing he could do but stay where he was until they came to get him. She could hardly wait to see his face when she walked in.

Over the years, Jennifer had speculated on Chad's looks. He would give her no help at all. It was amusing, really, how her image of him had changed through the years. As a child she pictured him as old, with white hair and kind-looking eyes. By the time she was a teenager he began to get younger in her eyes. After all, some of their discussions had been very open and frank. Somehow she couldn't see a kindly looking, white-haired gentleman telling her some of the things Chad had told her.

And now, she found herself treating him as a contemporary and an equal. Of course she loved him. How could she not love him? He had been so many things in her life. He'd been there for her, no matter what. But she had to admit that she felt a little peculiar about finally meeting him face-to-face after all this time.

She was glad that Tony was going to be along.

The office door opened and she turned around. Tony stood in the doorway. "You ready to go?"

She nodded.

"I borrowed a pickup. It won't be the smoothest riding vehicle, but we'll need the four-wheel drive once we get up into the mountains."

Jennifer followed him out of the room.

"I forgot to ask if you've eaten," he said as she passed.

"Yes."

"I think we'd better stop off at a convenience store somewhere and pick up something to take with us. There's not a whole lot between here and where we're going if we should get hungry or thirsty."

Poor Chad. She could imagine how he must be feeling, stranded out in the middle of nowhere, recovering from a head wound, without food. He hadn't said anything about water. She wondered about that.

They didn't waste any time at the store and were soon on the road. For the first several miles they were quiet, each lost in his and her own thoughts. Eventually Tony said, "I'm sorry we had to meet this way, Jennifer, but I'm glad that we finally have a chance to get acquainted after all this time. I'll admit I didn't recognize you from the first time I saw you."

She looked at him in surprise. As far as she knew, she had never seen this man in her life. "When did you ever see me?"

He glanced around briefly, then returned his eyes to the highway. "The same time Tiger did, when you were in the car wreck."

"The car wreck! Mother said I was only five when that happened."

"I know you were just a little thing. I felt so sorry for you."

"You and Chad were there?"

"Yes. We had been down in San Diego that day, just a couple of kids, really. I'd borrowed my dad's car and we'd gone down to see who we could impress, you know the kind things guys will do."

She smiled. "Not really, but it makes sense."

"We'd decided to stop and eat in Oceanside—Tiger knew a girl that lived somewhere around there and he was trying to figure out which house she lived in, so we were driving up and down the streets when we saw the car that came barreling around a corner and plowed into the one you and your family were in. God, it was awful . . . as I'm sure you remember."

She shook her head. "I don't remember much about it at all."

"We were the first ones there. It happened on the edge of town. There weren't many houses out that far. The guy that hit you was hurt bad, we could tell. And your mother and dad were pinned in the car." He shook his head. "I'd never seen anything like it. Tiger told me to go for help and he stayed there, trying to see what he could do. When I got back, I found him sitting beside the road holding you. He told me later you had been knocked unconscious in the back seat and when you woke up you became hysterical. He managed to get you out. So he sat there and held you until the police and the ambulance came."

"I never knew that."

"He was really upset, I can tell you. When they got your parents out and took all of you to the hospital, he insisted we follow. We stayed there at the hospital and waited to hear how you were doing."

"My mother told me my injuries weren't serious."

"That's what we found out. He worried about you later, though, when he heard that your dad didn't make it."

So her guardian angel had been a teenage boy when he first met her.

Tony continued to reminisce. "I remember that until we graduated from high school he would still go back down there and check on you."

"He did?"

"Sure. Don't you remember?"

How could she tell him that she didn't even remember what Chad looked like? She had no memory of him whatsoever.

"I know that he seemed interested in how I was doing," she said cautiously.

"He was. He used to talk about you all the time. The things you were doing, what you were learning in school. He was always so proud of you. I used to tease him about waiting around for you to grow up."

She glanced at him sharply. "He said that to me once."

"Then what's he been waiting for?" He gave her a glance from the corner of his eye. "You are certainly as grown-up as he could possibly want now."

Jennifer could not control the blush that she could feel flooding her face. "He admitted that he was only teasing me."

"You notice that he's never married anyone else, though," he pointed out in a wise tone. She glanced over at him and he winked.

No, she hadn't known that Chad wasn't married. She couldn't help feeling pleased at the idea that perhaps he had been waiting for her.

Then another thought struck her. "Are you married, Tony?" She would hate to have a jealous wife misunderstand her leaving town with Tony.

"I was. Unfortunately for me she found someone she wanted more, someone who wasn't spending all his time trying to make a living." He shrugged, but she could see the hurt that was still there. "I'm surprised Tiger trusted me with you, come to think of it. He's always telling me I have a terrible attitude toward women. Can't imagine why."

She smiled. "Obviously you're his best friend. Otherwise he wouldn't have sent me to find you."

"You're right. We go back a long way. When I called him and told him that a former business associate was trying to hassle me, he agreed to check it out for me. Neither of us thought it would turn out to be anything like this.''

"What does Chad do?''

He looked around at her in surprise. ''Don't you know?''

Jennifer had already accepted the fact that Tony did not know how she and Chad communicated. It was strange to think that she was closer to Chad than anyone in many ways and yet they were still strangers. She didn't want to have to explain their relationship to Tony, not if Chad hadn't already done so.

She tried to find a way to phrase her response that would not make the relationship even more confusing. "Chad is a very private person." Tony nodded his head. "Whenever I hear from him he chooses the topics we discuss. He doesn't like to talk about himself.''

"That's Tiger, all right. He's always been that way. Something of a loner. When we were in the Marines together we'd—''

"Chad was in the Marines?''

"Sure. We decided to go in right after we got out of high school. Why?''

"He never told me.''

"Oh. But he stayed in touch, didn't he?''

"Yes.''

"That's kinda odd, him not telling you. He always knew what you were up to. Maybe your mother wrote to him or something. When we were stationed overseas he spent a lot of time talking about you.''

Jennifer was having a tough time trying to put everything she was learning from Tony into perspective with what she already knew about Chad. He had lived a full and active life all the time he was in touch with her, and yet had never given her a hint of it.

She almost cringed at some of the childish questions and concerns she'd had back then. He had been so patient with her, kind and full of a sense of caring that had eased her over the rough spots in her life.

Oh, Chad, do you have any idea how much you mean to me?

"Obviously not enough to do what I ask. I thought I told you to let Tony come get me."

Jennifer tried to disguise the sudden start she gave when Chad responded. She shifted on the seat and glanced at Tony. "I think I'll try to catch a nap, if you don't mind. My day started out fairly early," she explained, trying to sound nonchalant.

"Good idea. Once we get off the main highway, the road is going to be too rough for you to do anything but hang on!"

Jennifer closed her eyes and willed herself not to speak out loud. *Chad? Can you hear me?*

"Of course I can hear you. What I want to know is why you aren't halfway back to L.A. by now?"

You know why. I wanted to see you.

"Has it ever occurred to you that perhaps I don't want to see you?"

Please don't be that way. Did you really come to see me when I was a child?

"Tony and his big mouth. Yes, Sunshine, I used to drive down there on a regular basis."

Then why don't I remember you?

"Because you never saw me. I used to sit outside the school and watch you come out. You were such a sad

little thing for a long while, but there was nothing I could do to help.''

But there was! You started talking to me.

"Yes. I realized that night of the accident when I tried to calm you down that I could pick up your thoughts—all your fear and terror. While I sat there holding you I not only talked to you, I tried to send you my thoughts to calm you. They seemed to help.''

I don't understand why I can't remember.

"You were just a baby. I don't think you'd even started school at that time. Later, whenever I thought of you, I discovered I could pick up on what you were thinking.''

Have you ever been able to do that with anyone else?

"No. But then I've never tried. Like I've told you. You're special.''

So are you.

"Come on, Sunshine, don't try to make me some sort of romantic hero. You wouldn't even like me if you knew me.''

How can you possibly say that?

"Because you have an image of me as someone very gentle. I'm not a gentle sort of person.''

You are with me.

"I know.''

She smiled slightly and drifted off to sleep.

Chapter Four

Tony was right. As soon as they turned off the paved road, Jennifer woke up.

"Road maintenance is a little slack in this area, wouldn't you say?" she managed to get out while bracing herself against the dashboard of the truck.

Tony chuckled. "I warned you."

"So you did. How much farther do we have to go?"

The sun had set and the evening light was rapidly fading. Tony flipped on the headlights, then glanced at his watch. "I haven't been here in a few years. It seems to me we have at least a couple of hours of this before we get there."

"No wonder Chad felt bruised and shaken."

"You know, I've been meaning to ask you. How did he manage to call and let you know what had happened to him? It doesn't really make sense, anyway. If he was going to contact anybody, why you? Why not me?''

Now what do I say? she asked Chad. There was no response. *Chad... Chad! What do you want me to tell him?*

"That's up to you."

"Thanks a lot!''

"What do you mean?" Tony asked, surprised at her tone of voice.

"Oh! For, uh, thinking that he should have called you instead of me, of course. That wasn't very kind of you.''

"Maybe not, but it makes sense. Why didn't he call me anyway?''

"Maybe he'd run out of quarters.''

"Besides, that place is so primitive, I can't believe there's a phone for miles.''

"Maybe it has a ham radio unit and he got some-one to relay it over a phone somewhere.''

"I suppose. I can always ask him when we get there.''

If we ever do, she thought, knowing that she was going to have bruises all over her bottom by the time they arrived, not to mention on her arms and legs.

"I tried to warn you."

"I know.''

"You know what?" Tony asked. "Is there some-thing wrong?''

"Not really. I suppose it's from being alone so much. I have a habit of talking to myself.''

Tony shook his head. Jennifer knew he was begin-ning to wonder about her. She looked out the win-dow, trying to hide her smile. Tony obviously didn't have too good an opinion of women anyway. She doubted if it would improve staying around her.

"I take it you live alone?" he asked after they had bounced along in silence for a few miles.

"Sort of. I share an apartment with a five-year-old cat named Sam." She would no more consider that she owned Sam than that he owned her. They had a workable relationship where each understood the other. Sam allowed her to feed him, pay his rent and keep him entertained. In turn, he looked after her, pointed out when she stayed out too late or tried to get away with oversleeping in the morning, and made judgments on any of her friends who happened to drop in.

"I thought about getting a pet, but I'm not home enough to look after one."

"Sam's been a lot of company to me. Since I don't travel much, he's never been much of a problem. This is the first time I've ever gone off and left him for a weekend."

"Aren't you afraid he'll get hungry?"

"Oh, no. I left him plenty of food and water. That's never the problem. He doesn't like being left alone. He's learned to tolerate it during the day, since he knows I have to work. But he gets very irritated when I'm out all evening. I have a feeling he's going to be irate by the time I get home."

"You know, there really wasn't any reason for you to come out here with me, once you let me know where he is."

"That's what Chad said," she muttered under her breath.

"Did you say something?"

"I was just agreeing with you. If I'd known what the roads were going to be like, I might have given more serious thought to returning home."

She turned her head to look at Tony and a brief flash of light caught her eye. She stared out the back window.

"Something wrong?" he asked.

"I thought I saw a light flash behind us."

Tony glanced up in the rearview mirror and they hit a particularly deep hole. Jennifer almost hit her head on the ceiling of the cab. "Sorry. I don't dare take my eyes off the road for a second. What sort of a light?"

She continued to watch out the back window. "I'm not sure. Could there be another car coming this way?"

"There could be, but it's rather hard to believe." He was quiet a moment. "Unless it's the same person or persons who brought Tiger out here and left him."

Jennifer discovered a knot in her chest that was making it difficult for her to breathe. She had no idea what she was getting into, but this wasn't her idea of a fun evening at all.

Tony cleared his throat nervously. "You know, this really isn't my style. I mean, I can handle myself all right in my own environment, but getting out here in the Great Outdoors—Well, Tiger's able to handle anything, anywhere. But not me."

"He wasn't able to handle this particular situation or he wouldn't be stuck out here."

"Don't rub it in, Sunshine."

"Keep watching and see if you catch a glimpse of that light again, okay?" Tony asked, continuing to concentrate on the road in front of them.

They were silent during the next hour, each watching the road—Tony the front, Jennifer the back. Twice she thought she saw a flicker of light, but the curving roads didn't reveal much.

"Not much farther now. I bet Tiger is going to be glad to see us."

Jennifer had been growing more and more tense. She didn't know how she was going to react when she saw Chad for the first time, particularly since he had made it clear that he didn't want her there. She was sorry she had insisted on coming along. After all, he had as much right to his privacy as she did to hers.

The light hadn't appeared in several miles and Jennifer decided that if it had been a car, the car had long since turned off, turned around or reached its destination.

"Ah hah!" Tony exclaimed with a sound of satisfaction. "He's got a light on, waiting for us." He pointed across a wide ravine and, perched on the side of a steep slope, she saw a small cabin with a dim, flickering light in the window.

"Are you sure that's the right place?"

"Fairly sure. Of course, we have several more miles to go to wind behind the ravine and get over there, but we're almost there."

By the time they pulled up in front of the cabin, Jennifer was shaking. As soon as the truck stopped, Tony jumped out of the cab and hollered, "Hey, Tiger, it's me—Tony."

The door of the cabin opened and a man stepped through, caught in the glare of the truck lights. Jennifer had no trouble seeing him very clearly.

He was tall, over six feet, with thick brownish-blond hair that was tousled. He wore khaki pants tucked into combat boots and a red-and-black-plaid shirt. The sleeves were rolled up to above his elbows, emphasizing his muscular arms. He stood there in the light, his hands resting casually on his hips and waited patiently for them to join him.

Jennifer could not seem to make herself move from where she sat inside the truck. Frozen, she continued to stare at the man who had been such an integral part of her life for the past twenty years.

Snatches of intimate conversations they had had came back to her and she cringed. How had she dared to be so open with him? He knew everything there was to know about her—her thoughts, her dreams, her ambitions.

She knew nothing about him. Most particularly she hadn't known that Chad was also the man she worked for, C. W. Cameron.

"You might as well get out of the truck, Jennifer, now that you're here," Chad said in a voice that clearly carried to where she sat.

How could he have done this to her? She continued to stare at him in shame and disbelief. There was no way she could have known. C. W. Cameron was nothing like Chad. Absolutely nothing.

She would never forget the first time she had been introduced to him. She had worked for his company as a stenographer for almost three months. Of course she had caught glimpses of him as he came in and out of his office, but that was all.

His assistant, Marlene, had recently announced her engagement to a man from Chicago and was happily making plans to move. Everyone had been wondering who would take her place. There was a chance someone might be promoted. Then again, they might look for someone outside the firm to fill the position.

When Jennifer was called into his office, she wasn't sure whether to be pleased or not. She hadn't been out of school long and probably had the least experience of anyone there.

C. W. motioned for her to sit down in the chair across from his desk. Timidly she perched on the edge of the chair. She glanced down to see what he was reading and saw her name on the folder. He must have gotten her file from personnel.

He glanced up without smiling. "I apologize for the delay in this meeting, Ms. Chisholm. I generally get acquainted with all of my employees within a few days after they arrive."

Jennifer forced herself to relax. So. She wasn't here to be interviewed for a new position. This was just a delayed welcome-on-board type of meeting.

C. W. continued, "I'm afraid things have been a little hectic lately and my schedule has not gone as smoothly as I would have wished."

Jennifer didn't know what to say, so she sat there with her hands clasped together in a death grip, trying to look relaxed, intelligent and at ease.

He glanced down at her folder, then back at her. "I notice that you made very high grades at the business college you attended."

"Yes, sir," she admitted shyly.

"I'm curious to know why you didn't go on to college."

She looked at him in surprise. "There weren't enough funds for that, I'm afraid, and it would have put an even greater burden on my mother. I needed to go to work as soon as possible."

"Have you thought about taking night courses?"

Again she looked at him in surprise. He was treating her more as a counselor would than an employer would.

"I'm not against that, of course. I just don't have a particular field I would be interested in pursuing."

"I see."

She could almost hear him thinking "no ambition." Perhaps that was true. She enjoyed her work and was quite content with it.

"You've done a remarkable job since you've been here, Ms. Chisholm," he offered quietly.

"Thank you."

"I have noticed, though, that when you transcribe my dictation it does not come back to me in the same form in which I dictate it."

Jennifer tried hard not to show how his comment affected her. She had tried to make only the revisions she felt absolutely necessary.

"You seem to feel the necessity to correct my grammar and my sentence structure from time to time," he pointed out in a dry voice.

She forced herself to meet his bland gaze, but she could read nothing. The golden eyes seemed to look right into the most vulnerable part of her being.

"Tell me, how did you hear about this job?"

Jennifer was surprised at the sudden change of subject.

"A friend at school mentioned that the agency was looking for stenographers. So I applied."

He continued to sit there, waiting, as though she had more to say. Jennifer had never seen a man who could be so still. His hands rested on the desk in front of him and she covertly studied them. They were large, strong hands. He was a large, strong man.

"Had you ever heard of the agency before? Or of me?"

She glanced up at his face again, startled by his questions.

"No, sir."

"You don't have to keep calling me 'sir,' you know. I may look old enough to be your father, but that's not quite the case."

The personal remark unnerved her, just as their whole conversation had done. She had never known anyone like him and didn't know how to respond to the man.

"Are you always so quiet?" he asked.

"When I don't have anything to say," she admitted.

He smiled and she was amazed at how the smile softened his harsh features. The smile quickly disappeared.

"I'd like you to begin working closely with Marlene for the next few weeks and learn her job before she leaves us, if that's agreeable with you."

Jennifer gasped. "Me?"

He glanced quickly over her shoulder, then his gaze pinned her to her chair. "I believe you're the only other person in the room. Why? Do you see some problem?"

"I, well, I, uh, no, not exactly. I mean, I don't have much experience and—" She couldn't think of anything else to say.

"I realize that. What I also realize is that despite your rather tender years, you show a great deal of initiative, intelligence, ability to grasp a new situation, willingness to work—in other words, all the attributes I want in an assistant. Do you want the job?"

Dazed, she stared back at him. Did she want the job? Did she want to work closely with this man every day? She knew so little about men. *Chad? What should I do?*

There was no answer. Chad was good at that. He might spend time with her going over her options, but he never made up her mind for her.

"Mr. Cameron, as you may well guess, this comes as quite a surprise to me." She searched for the right words. "If you don't mind, I'd like a day to think it over."

He watched her for a moment, then said, "Ah, yes. I did forget one rather important piece of information—your salary." He named a figure that doubled what she was presently making. "That's a beginning salary, of course. As you progress and take on more responsibility I will see that your raises reflect your increased worth to the company."

He stood up and she immediately got to her feet. "Perhaps you're right, Ms. Chisholm, to want to think this offer over. I will be waiting to hear your decision."

Jennifer barely remembered leaving his office and returning to her desk. She worked the rest of the day with no idea of what she was doing. Thank goodness the transcriptions of tapes had become so routine by then she could manage without her total concentration.

As soon as she got home that night and greeted Sam, who was still little more than a kitten at the time, she said, "Chad? I really need to talk to you."

"Go ahead, Sunshine. Talk."

Jennifer gave a sigh of relief. There were times when she couldn't get in touch with him, and she'd been afraid that tonight of all nights she wouldn't respond.

Kicking off her shoes she sat down in her favorite chair with a sigh.

"I got a terrific job offer today, Chad. I need to talk to you about it."

"I thought you just started a job."

"I did. It's the same place, only a different position. A much higher position. I'd be working as Mr. Cameron's assistant."

"Isn't he the fellow who runs the place?"

"That's right."

"Who is he?"

"What do you mean?"

"I mean, what do you know about him?"

"Not all that much, really, except for office gossip. He's single, attractive—"

"And that's why you'd go to work for him?" She could almost hear the disgust in his voice.

"Of course not. I'm not even sure I want to work for him, actually."

"What's the problem?"

"The problem is that I don't know that much about men. I don't remember my father that well. I never had any brothers. The boys I knew in school were more friends than anything. I think I'm a little afraid of him."

"You mean you think he'd chase you around the desk?"

She thought about that for a moment. "No, I don't think so. He doesn't seem to be the type of person. If he were, I'm sure the office staff would know about it. There's never been any talk about his personal life."

"Then what's to be afraid of?"

"He's so stern, so rigid. All business. He doesn't ever seem to relax."

"Maybe he's busy."

"I'm sure he is. I understand his dad opened the agency some years ago and when he was killed his son came home to run it." She got up and wandered into the kitchen and poured herself a glass of apple juice. "I'm sure that wasn't easy for him to do."

"Probably not. What had he been doing before then?"

"Nobody has ever said."

"I'm afraid I don't quite understand what you want from me, Sunshine."

"I'm not sure, either. I think I'm afraid of failing. The job has so much responsibility attached to it. I'm not sure I can handle it."

"Your boss must think you can or he wouldn't have offered you the position."

"I thought of that. I just don't know how he can tell so much about me. He doesn't know me at all."

"Maybe he's a good judge of character."

"What if I let him down?"

"But if you don't try, won't you be letting yourself down?"

"I suppose. I hadn't thought of it that way."

"Only you can decide what you want out life, you know. Nobody else can do that for you. If you're content working as a stenographer, if you don't want to learn anything more, then be the best stenographer you can be, and be happy doing it."

Jennifer was quiet for a few moments. "I guess I've still been blessing my opportunity to get a job as soon as I finished school. I hadn't looked any farther down the road than that."

"Now you're being challenged to look down that road to your future."

"Yes."

"Well, for the record, I believe in you, Sunshine. I know that you can do anything you decide you can do."

"Thank you, Chad. What would I do without you?"

"You'd do just fine and you know it."

The next morning she went into the office and told Mr. Cameron that she would be pleased to work as his administrative assistant.

Jennifer sat there in the truck, watching the two men talking. Slowly she opened the door and crawled out of the cab, already feeling the bruises on her backside. When she approached the two men they stopped talking and turned to her. Tony smiled, obviously pleased that they had found his friend. Chad, or C. W. Cameron, she wasn't sure how she was going to be able to think of him from now on, stood there waiting, watching her expression, revealing nothing of his thoughts to her. He never had. Only Chad had done that. Chad. She felt such a sense of loss that she almost crumpled with the pain. Chad, her lifelong friend, seemed to be gone. In his place stood the cold, aloof and distant man she had worked for all these years.

She didn't know what to say.

C. W. Cameron suddenly smiled, a warm, relaxed smile that caused a feeling of light and energy to flood over her. He took a couple of steps toward her and enfolded her in his arms. Holding her close, he laid his cheek on the top of her head. "You finally found me out, didn't you, Sunshine?"

Chapter Five

Jennifer's ear was pressed hard against Chad's chest and she could feel the heavy thumping of his heart inside. She had never been so close to him before, never felt the strength of him.

Raising her head she looked into his eyes. They were guarded, but there was a hint of emotion that she had never seen before. "How are you feeling?" she managed to say. Her voice sounded weak and trembling.

"I'll feel better once we get away from this place. If you hadn't arrived, things could have gotten a little desperate. There's nothing to eat up here and the nights get a little cold, even in August."

"Did you have some water?"

"Yes. There's a well."

Tony spoke up. "We've got food in the truck. I don't see any reason to hang around here, do you?"

Chad glanced over at him. "No, I don't. Especially if you think you've been followed."

The three of them started for the truck, but Chad hadn't let go of his grip around Jennifer. He had tucked her under his arm, his hand clamped against her waist, holding her to his side.

Jennifer clambered into the truck quickly and sat in the middle. The men hastily followed, slamming their doors. Tony had automatically slid behind the wheel again, leaving Chad to sit beside her. Because of the floor shift, Jennifer found herself plastered against Chad's side. His arm was draped on the seat behind her. She wriggled, trying to place some distance between the two of them. His hand fell on her shoulder, effectively pinning her to his side. *"You're fine, just where you are."*

Of course. He still knew what she was thinking. He had always known, even when they were working together. Never by any hint had he given away his extra knowledge of her. She wondered how he'd managed.

"It wasn't easy, Sunshine, believe me."

She darted a glance in his direction, but he wasn't looking at her. Instead he had leaned forward and was digging into the sack at his feet. "Ah, food." Reaching down into the sack he pulled out a plastic-wrapped sandwich. With a grin he handed it to her. "How about opening this for me, would you? I'm short of hands at the moment."

Since his left hand was curved around her shoulder and he gave no indication that he would ever move it, she recognized that he preferred their current position over eating, despite how hungry he was.

Without saying anything, she unwrapped the sandwich and held it out to him. He seemed to inhale it. She reached down and found the six-pack of soda they had bought and without asking, opened one of them for him.

"Thanks," he muttered, taking a long swallow and exhaling with a sigh.

"What do you think is going on?" Tony asked.

That was what Jennifer wanted to know, but she had a hunch they were concerned about two different subjects.

"The way I figure it, your friend didn't appreciate all my questions. I was sent out here on a wild-goose chase."

"Where did they force you off the road?"

"I don't know. I've never been out here before. It was long before we left the highway, though," Chad replied. He began to massage Jennifer's neck and shoulders, his fingers pushing and kneading the stiff muscles. They hit a sudden bump and he held her against him for a moment, then eased his grip and began to stroke across her shoulders again.

"I didn't see any sign of your car."

Chad sighed. "I'm not surprised. I didn't have a chance to remove the keys. There were three men in the car. Only two brought me up here. My car will probably turn up abandoned somewhere."

"Do you think they intended to let you die up here?" Jennifer asked.

"Who knows? I didn't make any friends when I hit the first guy. That's when I must have gotten clobbered from behind. By the time I came to I was in the back seat with a pistol aimed at me and we were on this road. My biggest fear was that one of the holes in the road would cause that pistol to go off. You can bet I stayed as quiet as possible.''

Tony laughed. ''Actually, you look a hell of a lot better than I expected. I can remember some of the scrapes we used to get into when—''

''Yeah. Me, too, Tony. But I'd rather not go into them at the moment.''

Jennifer felt his gaze rest on her profile but she refused to look up at him. He still didn't want her knowing any more about him than he could help, which she found extremely annoying, under the circumstances. He knew everything about her.

''Not everything, Sunshine.''

She forced herself not to answer him out loud. Tony didn't need to know what was between them. *Why didn't you ever let me know who you were were?*

''How could I? Remember, it wasn't my idea for you to come to work at the agency. It took me a few weeks to overcome the shock of finding you working for me, and another few weeks to decide that despite everything, you were the best employee I had.''

She remembered now that he had questioned her on her choice of coming to work there. At the time they were having a high turnover of employees. Since then, the problems had been worked out and the work force was much more stable.

''People still move away and have babies. That's the norm for the working world these days,'' he continued.

If you didn't want me working for you, why did you make me your administrative assistant?

"I didn't say I didn't want you working for me. I said it was a shock. Like I told you, despite our relationship, you were the most suited for the position. The personnel director suggested you to me, although I had already recognized how well you edited my tapes as you went along."

I thought you were upset about that.

"I was more amused than anything. You have such a keen mind. You constantly amaze me. You might be shy in other areas, but when you know you're right you do what you have to do."

I am not shy.

"Of course you are. You rarely date."

Whose fault is that? she demanded, glancing up at him out of the corner of her eye.

Chad had been eating another sandwich while she held his soda. Now he took it from her, deliberately trailing his fingers across hers.

"I never stopped you from dating. You and Jerry seemed to have a good relationship."

A friendly relationship, that's all.

"What's wrong with being friends?"

Not a thing.

"Are you still blaming me for telling you Larry Donahue was married?"

Of course not! She thought back for a few minutes. *Wait a minute. You're the one who introduced me to Larry.*

"Right. But I didn't expect you to date the man just because I introduced him to you."

Then why didn't you say something there in the office?

"Because we don't have that sort of relationship in the office."

Jennifer grew quiet. So much had hit in the past hour that her head was still reeling. What was going to happen to her now? Nothing in her life was going to be the same again.

"That's the way life works, Sunshine. Nothing ever stays the same. We wouldn't want it to, now would we? That's part of our growth pattern—to learn, to gain wisdom, to expand."

I was perfectly content to leave things the way they were.

"Oh, were you now? Who was it who insisted on coming up here to finally meet Chad? Who was so gleeful that you had found me in a position where I had no choice? You wanted to know. Now you do."

Now I do, she repeated a little sadly.

"And you're disappointed." Chad shifted. She could feel the long length of his leg pressed against hers. Since he had taken the can of soda out of her hand, it was free. She could almost feel the hurt that he was experiencing at the thought that she was disappointed to learn his true identity. She shifted her hand until it rested on his thigh.

Not disappointed. Shocked is more the word. When I think of the times—

"Don't think of them."

How can I possibly forget them? You listened patiently while I carried on and on about how cold and unfeeling my boss was. You must have had a tough time not revealing how amusing you found me.

"I wasn't amused, Sunshine. I could feel your frustration with the situation. Unfortunately, what

you were dealing with was the real me out in the business world.''

Nonsense. You are not cold and unfeeling. You are warm and caring and— Jennifer caught her breath as the memory of his earlier words came back to haunt her. He had told her that he loved her. He had told her that he had always loved her. Chad loved her. That meant that C. W. Cameron also loved her. She was dazed by the thought.

He sat quietly beside her, refusing to comment on her most recent thoughts. She was almost grateful.

The two men began to talk and Jennifer gratefully tuned out their conversation. Her mind was in such turmoil. In all the years that she had tried to guess at the type of person Chad was, she would never have pictured him as a no-nonsense businessman, brisk and efficient.

Jennifer let her head rest wearily against his shoulder. Too many things had come at her too quickly for her to take them in. She allowed her eyes to close, enjoying his solid warmth beside her. She would have to think about everything later.

By the time they reached the smoother surface of the highway, Jennifer was sound asleep in Chad's arms.

Later Jennifer vaguely recalled being lifted and held close and a sense of movement, but that was all. She had been so tired. And why not? She'd made the drive from Los Angeles, plus the additional one into the Utah mountains. She'd been bounced and bruised and she had met her lifelong friend in the flesh, which had been traumatic, to say the least.

The next thing she knew was that she was lying in bed, the covers tucked cozily around her.

"Sunshine? Are you awake yet?"

Drowsily her eyes opened. She was in a strange room. Rolling onto her back she saw that she was in a hotel room. The drapes were closed and there was very little light in the room. Bewildered, she sat up and the covers slipped to her waist. Only her scraps of underwear kept her from being totally unclothed.

"Chad!"

"Ah, so you are awake. Good, I—"

"What did you do with my clothes!"

"?"

"And don't play the innocent with me."

"If you will look on the chair in front of the window, you will find them neatly folded and waiting for you to put on."

She saw them just where he described.

"Oh."

"Did you bring any others with you?"

"Yes, but they're in the car."

"And the car is—?"

"Parked in the Lucky Lady's parking lot. You had no right to take off my clothes, Chad."

"No right? Come on, Sunshine. You sound like some Victorian lady. You wouldn't have rested in those jeans and you know it. Are you afraid I took advantage of you while you slept?"

"Fat chance."

She could feel his amusement. *"Would you like to meet me for brunch? Several of the casinos around town put on an excellent spread."*

Jennifer tried to see what time it was, but it was too dark.

"Almost ten."

That late! And she had to get back to Los Angeles. After all, she had a job to do and—Her job! Suddenly she remembered all that she had learned the previous day.

"Are you afraid I'll fire you if you don't get back to work in time?"

She didn't know what to think. Never had she been so confused. "I'm going to take a shower. I should be ready in about half an hour."

"Fine."

She hopped out of bed and went into the bathroom. Everything in the two rooms was clean and of the highest quality. The hotel had thoughtfully provided shampoo and deodorant as well as a shower cap if she didn't want to take time to wash her hair.

Jennifer had no choice. She felt grimy after the dusty ride on the back roads yesterday. The hot water felt wonderful beating down on her and she forced her mind to relax and enjoy it. She had time enough later to try to figure out what to do with all the new information she'd just received.

Eventually she faced that she would have to leave the security of the shower. Wrapping her dripping hair in a towel she stepped out of the tub and started drying off.

"Sunshine?"

She kept drying. "Are my thirty minutes up?"

"No, but I brought your suitcase in for you. Do you need anything out of it?"

Her suitcase—with her toothbrush, her hair dryer, her—"Where are you?"

"In your room. Where else would I be?"

Hastily she draped the large towel around her and jerked open the bathroom door. Peering around the corner she saw her suitcase on her rumpled bed and Chad sitting on the chair by the window.

He had obviously spent a restful night. His hair appeared slightly damp from the shower, and his clothes looked fresh. Today he wore a pair of Levi's that fit him embarrassingly well, and a white, long-sleeved shirt that once again had the sleeves turned up above the elbows. He was sitting stretched out in the chair, his legs extended and crossed at the ankle. Today he wore moccasins. His elbows rested on the high arms of the chair and his hands made a steeple under his chin.

She had never seen C. W. Cameron dressed in anything but three-piece business suits that effectively concealed his well-developed body. Nothing Chad had on today hid much of anything. The top three buttons of his shirt were open and she could see the soft golden hair revealed there.

When her gaze met his eyes she saw that he was amused at the long study she was giving him. He hadn't been wasting his time, either, obviously enjoying the view as she stood there with a towel wrapped under her arms and hanging to mid-thigh.

"How did you get in?"

"I have a key, why?"

"No reason, I guess. Thank you for getting my clothes for me."

"My pleasure." The way he drawled the words and the look he had on his face as his eyes continued to wander from her towel-draped head to her bare toes made her grab her suitcase and hurry back to the bathroom.

She could hear his laughter through the closed door.

Jennifer did not find the present situation particularly amusing. To think that all this time she had been working for Chad and he had known...

She saw her wide-eyed expression in the mirror and almost groaned out loud. How could he?

That time two years ago when she had gotten so angry at Mr. Cameron, she had almost quit. In fact, if it hadn't been for Chad insisting she simmer down before making any decisions...

Of course he'd been right. No one should make decisions when they were angry. A person wasn't really thinking when angry. But oh! How she had wanted to quit. He had been so arrogant, so rude.

He'd also been putting in long, grueling hours, and he'd had several clients come in demanding immediate help. At the time she had not seen the situation from his side. All she knew was that he was demanding impossibly long hours from her. Yet he'd been there working right alongside her.

What would have happened if Chad hadn't calmed her down and she'd given notice? Would she have been any happier anywhere else?

The answer was no, of course. She enjoyed her work. She found it challenging. Now that she recalled that particular incident, she remembered that she was surprised the next day when Mr. Cameron had asked her to go to lunch with him to discuss some business matters that he preferred not to have interrupted by the constant ringing of the phone.

They had sat for two hours while he discussed the present crisis in the office. He had asked her advice on how to handle the sudden influx of business, and he had listened when she made a few suggestions. Before long, each of them was coming up with ideas built on the other's suggestions. By the time they returned to the office Jennifer had totally forgotten that she had seriously considered resigning. He had stopped in front of her desk while she put her purse away. When she sat down he was still standing there.

"Thank you for a very valuable lunch, Ms. Chisholm. I hope we can get some of these ideas working for us immediately. They should help the wear and tear on our nerves."

She smiled at him, aware of the strain in his face. "I hope so, too, Mr. Cameron."

No sooner had she gotten home that night and been greeted by Sam when Chad had gotten in touch with her.

"Well, Sunshine? Did you resign today?"

"No, of course not."

"Why do you say, 'of course not'? Didn't you tell me last night that you no longer wanted to work for an arrogant, rude, bullying slave driver of a boss and that you weren't sure you'd even be able to stay for the two weeks necessary to work out your notice?"

"I overreacted."

"You mean he isn't any of those things?"

"He's tired, Chad. Really worn out. The poor man has been trying to do the work of three people. I think I convinced him today to hire at least one more investigator, possibly two, to help with the work load. He's seriously considering it."

"What a difference a day makes. Yesterday he was arrogant and rude. Today he's a poor man."

"You can make fun of me all you want. Once I calmed down, I realized that I only saw what was happening to me, what I was going through, how mistreated I was. Today, he gave me an opportunity to look at it from his point of view. He's never asked more of me than he's asked of himself. In fact, he generally puts in longer hours than I do, since he's out in the field so much as well as in the office digging through the piles of paper alongside of me."

Now as Jennifer put on the finishing touches of her makeup and made sure her slip didn't show under the dress she had hastily packed, she realized how many times she and Chad had discussed her relationship with her boss.

How embarrassing. No wonder he as her boss had no trouble understanding her. If only she'd been given the same opportunity. But she had, actually. As Chad he had explained his position as much as he could without revealing his identity. He had given her an opportunity to see inside of him, to share his thoughts and feelings.

Jennifer placed her hand lightly on her breasts, where the tiny butterfly fluttering seemed to have started. She and Chad had been much more intimate over the years than other people. They had never shared a physical intimacy, but that seemed almost superfluous to what they already had.

She knew he loved her and was there for her, just as he had known when he had contacted her that she would do anything to help him, no matter what it was. They had experienced a true union of their innermost spirits by the long-familiar exchange of their thoughts and feelings.

How could she say she didn't know the man sitting out there waiting so patiently for her? She knew him as well as she knew herself.

And she loved him with a depth of feeling that almost shook her with its intensity.

Jennifer opened the door and stepped out into the room. Chad had his eyes closed and he opened them when he heard the door. She knew that the dress she wore was the same color as her eyes. It was a simple cotton sundress that she generally wore to the beach or to go shopping. Not wanting to take much time with her hair, she had combed it back from her face and let it wave to her shoulders.

Chad never took his eyes off her as he slowly came to his feet and walked over to her. She could smell the light scent of his after-shave, and she realized how familiar the smell had become to her over the years. Many times, before she looked up, she had known when he'd returned to the office by that special scent.

Now she carefully explored his face with her intent gaze—his thick brows that almost met across his nose; his deep-set, hooded eyes, that seemed to glow with a secret fire of their own; his nose, that looked as though it had been broken more than once; his high cheekbones and square jaw. She saw the honesty and integrity stamped on his face, the experiences life had tossed his way, how little joy he had found so far, and how little he really expected to find.

Jennifer went up on tiptoe and slid her arms around his neck. "Oh, Chad, I love you so much," she whispered with trembling lips as she placed them on his firm, well-shaped mouth.

Chapter Six

Chad put his arms around her as a drowning man would grab a life preserver. They clung to each other, his mouth parting hers and taking possession as though he had spent years of dreaming about the opportunity. No one had ever kissed Jennifer that way before. She had been used to gentle, friendly kisses.

There was nothing gentle nor particularly friendly about what he was doing at the moment. Chad was making his claim to her clear. He lifted her in his arms and carried her back to the large stuffed chair he had recently vacated and sank down without ever losing contact with her mouth. His tongue searched and explored her mouth—lightly tracing the slightly uneven line of her teeth, coaxing her tongue to meet his in a playful duel. It was as though he had waited forever for the opportunity to get to know her as well physically as he knew her mentally and emotionally.

His hand rested at her throat. When he began to explore the contour of her face with his lips, placing tiny kisses in a careful row, his hand slowly inched downward until it rested on her breast.

Jennifer had never experienced so many intense emotions at once. She was shaking with reaction. Never in her wildest imaginings did she expect to feel so on fire. Everywhere he touched a combustive flame seemed to flare up between them. She shifted restlessly in his arms.

He clamped his arm around her waist. "Be still," he said sharply.

Her eyes snapped open. That was the least loverlike command she'd ever heard.

"I'm having all I can do to hang on to my self-control as it is, Sunshine," he advised her with a rueful grin.

Jennifer wanted to disappear in a puddle of embarrassment. Of course she knew all the clinical details regarding sex, but at the moment she hadn't been thinking about those facts.

Hastily getting to her feet, she straightened her dress and attempted to smooth her hair where his hand had ruffled it only a few moments before.

"I suppose we should go get something to eat," she managed to say while trying to steady her breathing.

He grinned. "I suppose we should," he mimicked softly. "Otherwise, we might not leave this room for the rest of the day."

She whirled away from him in an attempt to hide the expression on her face. How could she tell him that she wouldn't mind at all spending the rest of the day in bed with him?

"Why, Sunshine, I'm shocked to hear such lascivious thoughts coming from your pure and chaste mind."

Oh, no! She had forgotten how clearly he could read her mind. Turning to face him, knowing that her face must be a lovely shade of fiery red, she said, "Stop it, Chad. I can't seem to block you out of my mind the way you do me. But don't you dare tease me about my thoughts, do you understand?"

He stood up and faced her from across the room, his smile gone, his expression serious. "I'm sorry, Jennifer. I wasn't making fun of you, please believe me. I was trying to lighten the volatile atmosphere, if possible. You see, this is why I knew a relationship between us would never work. Everyone needs their privacy, even from their closest loved one. I don't want to destroy what we have in the hopes of having more."

Picking up her purse and pocketing the room key, Chad handed her the purse and opened the door. "I want to make love to you very much, but not at the expense of everything else we've always shared. I won't ever sacrifice that, do you understand me?"

He closed the door and politely guided her down the hall, his hand resting lightly at her waist.

Jennifer realized that she seldom heard him call her Jennifer. She had always been Sunshine to him—or Ms. Chisholm. For a shocked moment she felt a loss so intense she could scarcely comprehend it. What would it be like never to be called Sunshine again? That had been a very special name between them that no one else had ever known.

She understood what he was saying to her. Their physical response to each other was astonishing, like wildfire racing before the wind. But she wasn't willing to give up their unique relationship in order to experience the full expression of their physical love for each other.

When they reached the lobby of the hotel, Jennifer recognized that they were next door to Tony's casino. A blast of hot air hit them when they stepped outside.

"Do you mind if we take your car? Mine hasn't been found yet," Chad said, as though nothing out of the ordinary had happened between them.

Jennifer nodded, her thoughts still engrossed in all the discoveries she'd been making—about herself, her beliefs, and about Chad.

They made idle conversation over brunch. Jennifer had never seen so much food at one time before.

"Haven't you ever been to Las Vegas before?" Chad asked later, sipping his coffee.

"No. It isn't the sort of place you'd visit alone."

"True. Maybe we should plan to stay another night and I'll show you around."

She glanced down at her dress. "I'm afraid I didn't bring anything dressy to wear."

"That's no problem. We can always find something here, if you'd like."

Jennifer grinned. What better way to see Las Vegas than with your best friend? Add to that the fact that he was also your boss and was giving you permission not to be at work the next day and she could find nothing in his suggestion to complain about.

"I would love it." She stood up and held out her hand. "I can hardly wait to get started. Let's go."

He laughed at her enthusiasm, and for a moment Jennifer stared at him in astonishment. She had never seen C. W. Cameron laugh. Never. She had seen an occasional smile, but that was all. Now he looked happy and relaxed. She was amazed at the transformation.

Hugging his arm as they went out the door, Jennifer decided to make that day the most special day of her life. She knew without consciously acknowledging it that they might not have many of them together.

Chad must have made a similar resolution. Never had Jennifer seen C. W. Cameron so relaxed before. His smile came easily as she took him on a tour of the stores, modeling the most outrageous and the most demure outfits for him. She found that she enjoyed making him laugh or catching him by surprise.

As a joke she tried on a flame-red dress that molded her curves, leaving a long length of leg showing. Hastily digging in her purse she found some hairpins and gathered her hair into a rather precarious topknot on top of her head. Casual curls fell in front of her ears and along the nape of her neck. Thankful that her heels were high enough to effectively show off the dress, Jennifer sauntered out of the dressing room to where Chad waited.

Later she wished she'd had a camera trained on his face when he saw her. He did a perfect example of a double take. He was sitting in a chair and she ambled over to him and leaned down, knowing the top of her dress would fall open.

"You look a trifle bored, cowboy. Care for a little action?" she said in a low voice.

His gaze zeroed in on the front of her dress, then bounced up to meet hers. Jennifer thoroughly enjoyed watching the color wash over his cheeks, then recede.

"I don't think that's quite, uh, you, Sunshine," he said in a strangled voice.

She straightened, running her hand from her waist down to her thigh. "Oh, I don't know. Just feel this material. Isn't it something?" Gently picking up his hand where it was clenched on the arm of the chair, she placed his hand on her thigh.

Chad jerked his hand back as though the dress had been as hot as its color indicated.

"What are you doing?" he asked in a gruff whisper.

"Trying to find something to wear for tonight, honey," she drawled, trying not to laugh.

"Well, that won't do at all."

She assumed a disappointed air. "Oh, that's too bad. I always thought that red was definitely my color."

Without looking at him Jennifer sashayed back into the dressing room. She was chuckling as soon as she reached the small cubicle. Curious to see if she could, Jennifer tried to focus in on his thoughts, in a way similar to what he said he had done with her years ago.

All the time she was taking off the red dress and trying on the next one, she concentrated. Slowly she began to pick up his amazement and confusion at her behavior, as well as his embarrassment.

What's the matter, cowboy? Can't you take a little teasing?

"Is that what that was?" he responded promptly.

I always wondered how I'd do as a dance hall girl.

"You'd be a sensation. However, I don't think my heart could handle much of that."

You'll like this one much better, she assured him.

He did. The blue-green material shifted color like the ocean on a sunny day. The dress fit her snugly to the waist, then flared to a swirling skirt that emphasized her trim legs.

She felt his sigh of relief when she walked out. Her smile was impish. "Is this better?"

"Much," he said with conviction.

After paying for her purchase with her credit card they were soon back on the street.

"Tony asked us to drop in this afternoon if we had time."

"I'd love that." Jennifer recognized that no matter what they did, she would love it. She enjoyed being with Chad, getting to know the physical side of him. C. W. Cameron was still very much in evidence, but the shock had worn off and she was catching glimpses of the Chad she knew and loved beneath the gruff exterior of her employer.

When they reached the ornate lobby of the Lucky Lady, Jennifer paused and looked up at Chad. "Why don't you go on up while I stop in the rest room for a moment?"

"Would you like me to wait?"

She shook her head, still a little shy with him. "That's not necessary. I need to freshen my makeup and it will probably take a few minutes. But I promise not to be too long."

Chad leaned down and kissed her softly on the lips, disregarding anyone who might be watching. "I'll see you upstairs, then."

When Jennifer sat down in front of the mirror, she hardly recognized the glowing woman in front of her. Her hair seemed to have a vitality all its own, her eyes sparkled and glittered, even her skin seemed to have taken on a special glow. Love was the best beauty aid going, she decided with a grin.

Hastily renewing her lipstick and powdering away the shine on her nose and forehead, Jennifer left the ladies' lounge and started toward the elevator. Before she realized what was happening, two men, one on each side of her, took her arm and propelled her through the front door of the casino and into a waiting limousine just outside the door.

"Wha—? Wait a minute. What are you doing?" The car pulled away from the curb and quickly joined the traffic along the Strip.

"Don't worry, lady. Nobody's going to hurt you," one of the men said. She glanced around the car. Jennifer had never seen so much luxury in an automobile before. The driver wore a uniform and cap and the men on either side of her were in dark suits and wore sunglasses.

Chad!

"What is it? Where are you?"

I don't know where I am or where I'm going. Two men just grabbed me as I started toward the elevator and they're hauling me away in a luxury car.

"Who are they?"

I have no idea.

She could feel his fear and anger wash over her, and she almost flinched away from its intensity.

"We're not going to hurt you, lady," the man repeated. "Our boss wants to see you."

"Who is your boss?"

He looked at her without expression. In a flat tone he replied, "He'll tell you, himself."

"Where are you now?"

I don't know. We just passed the Tropicana and seem to be heading out of town.

"Don't worry, Sunshine. I'm right behind you. What does the car look like?"

Uh, it's silver. She glanced around. *Has some sort of antenna on the trunk.*

The car picked up speed once it left the town area. Jennifer didn't want to give away the fact that they might be followed, so she forced herself to continue looking straight ahead. There wasn't much to see. Occasionally there would be a house enclosed in a high fence. Most of them had swimming pools, which Jennifer didn't find too surprising. The desert was a good place to spend time in the water.

They made a sharp right turn onto a smaller road that took them farther from any other signs of houses. Eventually they pulled up in front of a heavy gate. The driver spoke into a small hand-held mike and the doors slowly opened. As soon as the car passed through, Jennifer turned around and watched the gate close. The gate was the only break in a tall, stone wall that seemed to encircle a multiacre area.

After following a winding road for several minutes, the car eased to a stop in front of a sprawling, one-story home in adobe and red tiles, that was designed for Southwest living. The home was beautiful but Jennifer wasn't in the mood to stand around and admire it.

She was escorted with a great deal of courtesy into the house and was thankful for the air-conditioning that greeted her at the double-doored entrance. One of the men showed her into a large room, which had one wall of glass and overlooked a giant swimming pool. The water looked very inviting.

The sound of ice tinkling in a glass caused her to turn around. A middle-aged woman holding a tray of drinks smiled and said, "I brought you something to drink."

Jennifer smiled. "Thank you." She walked over to the tray, which had been placed on a round coffee table. There was quite a selection to choose from. She poured herself some iced tea from a pitcher, added lemon and sipped the liquid absently.

"Where are you?"

Behind a massive stone wall. Did you ever see the car?

"I got a glimpse, but that's all. Did you turn off the main road?"

Yes. We turned right, just past a white, two-story house on the left that had a cyclone fence. Did you see that?

"Damn. Yes. I passed it a few miles back. Who's there?"

No one at the moment.

"Try to stall them until I get there."

Chad! There's no way you can get onto the grounds. The wall is massive.

"I'll check it out. Just be careful. When you have any more information, let me know."

She wandered around the room, sipping her tea and enjoying the objets d'art that spoke of expensive tastes. Jennifer couldn't believe her attitude toward what had happened. At first she had been startled, then frightened—until she had made contact with Chad. After that, she had calmed down. She knew she wasn't in any danger. She had been treated with courtesy and kindness at all times, except for having been whisked out of the Lucky Lady by a couple of strangers.

Plus she had a great deal of faith in Chad's ability. Jennifer had to admit that she was curious as to what was going on. She had a hunch she'd be told eventually.

When a man walked into the room, Jennifer was ensconced in a comfortable chair, gazing out at the garden surrounding the pool.

"I'm sorry to have kept you waiting, Ms.—" He paused, waiting for her response.

Jennifer's gaze returned from the garden and made an inspection of the man standing before her. He lacked several inches of being six foot, but he made up in girth for his lack of height. She had to admit that his excellent tailoring did its best to conceal his obesity. Her eyes wandered to his face, which was as round as his body, and met a pair of black eyes that seemed to have seen everything in the world and would no longer be surprised at anything else they might see. His gray hair was thinning badly, despite his attempts to disguise it.

Without getting up, she said, "Jennifer Chisholm," in a quiet voice. "And you are—?"

"Max Taylor. You may have heard of me."

"Yes, Mr. Taylor, I've heard your name before. Are you responsible for my sudden visit here?"

He laughed, obviously amused at her attitude. "Yes. This is my home."

"Is this your usual way of getting company when you're bored, Mr. Taylor?" she asked before taking another sip of her drink.

He sank down into a chair opposite hers with a sigh. "Not usually, no. I'm just tired of Tony's games, that's all."

"And what do I have to do with Tony's games?"

"I'm not sure. That's what I intend to find out."

"Why me?"

"Because you're the only woman Tony's been around lately. I figured if I brought you out here, he might be willing to talk to me. Up until now, he has refused my calls."

She nodded her head sagely. "I see. I'm supposed to be your calling card, is that it?"

He grinned. "I suppose you could put it that way."

"Obviously you don't know Tony very well. He doesn't care for women."

"Now, wait a minute. I've known Tony Carillo for years. You aren't trying to tell me that he's—"

"Uh, no, Mr. Taylor. That isn't what I meant. He's a little bitter at the moment, that's all. Obviously you have mistaken me for his girlfriend. I'm not."

"But you managed to see him yesterday when no one else has been able to get to him in months. He's holed himself up in that casino and refuses to talk to anyone."

"If you could talk with him, Mr. Taylor, what is it you would want to say?"

"That's between me and him."

"Okay."

They sat there for a few moments in silence. Jennifer once again began to admire the beauty of the garden.

"I figure Tony should be trying to call me any time now," Max finally muttered.

She glanced around and smiled. "Don't count on it, Mr. Taylor. Your men were so slick at whisking me out of the casino no one knows where I went."

"But Tony will miss you and begin asking questions."

"Hardly. Tony doesn't even know me. The only reason I saw him yesterday was to find my—er, boss, C. W. Cameron." Jennifer began to put some things together. "Do you by chance own some land and a small cabin in southern Utah?"

He looked at her suspiciously. "So what if I do?"

She shrugged. "I just wondered. That's where Tony and I found Mr. Cameron last night."

Max suddenly sat up straighter. "You mean that man that was nosing around—You mean Tony sent him to—Are you telling me you found that place?"

"I wouldn't presume to tell you a thing, Mr. Taylor. Nor would I want to point out to you that kidnapping is a federal offense." She took another sip of her tea and returned her gaze to the beauty of the outdoors.

"Who is this Mr. Cameron?" he demanded.

She turned her head. "I told you. He's my boss."

"What was he doing snooping around me?"

"I don't know. You'll have to ask him."

"What does that mean?"

"Just that he'll be here demanding some answers from you before too long. Hope you have them for him. He can be very demanding." She sighed. "A very difficult man to work for, I'll admit." Her limpid blue gaze met his. "But the job does have certain compensations."

For a heavy man, Max Taylor moved with surprising agility. He strode out of the room and she could hear his voice calling someone as he stormed down the hall.

Idly she wondered if she'd hurt his feelings. Here he was being such a kind host. Oh, well. Maybe he'd have to find someone else to make friends with.

"Sunshine?"

Oh, hi, Chad. My host's name is Max Taylor. He knows Tony and seems to feel Tony is avoiding him. He's also the man who owns the cabin in the mountains where we found you.

"Damn."

Where are you?

"I've found the place. I was hoping that I wouldn't have to storm it, though."

I can ask him to let me go. He seems a very accommodating fellow.

"He's anything but that, believe me. He's ruthless. That's why Tony got out of the partnership with him. He doesn't like the way he runs his business."

Oh. Jennifer had a sudden hunch she shouldn't have been baiting the man.

"What did you say to him?" Chad demanded.

Oh, nothing much. Reminded him that kidnapping was a federal offense.

"That's great, Sunshine. Nothing like reminding him that he's in deep water now." He was silent for a moment. *"You aren't even scared!"*

No. This is kind of fun, you know? Nothing very exciting has happened to me my whole life. Now in one weekend all kinds of things are happening. Maybe you should let me come out in the field with you more often.

She wasn't sure, but she was almost certain that what she felt was a groan in response.

"*Sunshine?*"

Yes?

"*Please don't antagonize the man. I've got to get in touch with Tony and see if he can shed any light on this.*"

Good idea. He said he expected Tony to call now that he had his girlfriend.

"*What!*"

Yes. That's why he had me grabbed, to get back at Tony. Isn't that amusing?

"*I don't find a damned thing funny about any of this. Why should he think there's something going on between you and Tony?*"

I suppose because I was shown up to see Tony yesterday when I first arrived. No one else has been able to get through to him.

"*I told you that.*"

Yes, I know. So now Max thinks Tony and I are sweethearts.

"*Maybe we can use that. Just sit tight, Sunshine. I'll be in touch.*"

She smiled. "I know."

"Who are you talking to?" Max demanded, as he stomped back into the room.

"No one."

"I heard you talking to someone. Are you bugged?"

She glanced down at the sundress she was wearing. "No. I just have a habit of talking to myself. That comes from living alone too long." She looked at him and smiled. "Is there a chance I could go lie down somewhere for a while? I didn't get much sleep last night."

Max eyed her suspiciously. She met his gaze with a very innocent smile. Abruptly he turned, motioning her to follow. The hall they followed was spacious and long. Eventually Max paused and opened a door. The drapes were pulled and the room was in cool shadows. As luxurious as the rest of the house, the elaborate decor seemed to imply that whatever was troubling Max, it wasn't the lack of money.

She nodded her head. "Thank you, Mr. Taylor." Closing the door quite gently in front of him, she heaved a sigh of relief and went over to the bed. Slipping off her shoes she stretched out on the bed. "Okay, Chad. I've taken myself off to a bedroom for a nap. That should keep me out of trouble."

There was a long pause. She wasn't sure he had heard her. *"Good idea,"* came back distractedly. *"I'll see you soon."*

Obviously his mind was on other things, such as how to get her out of Max Taylor's home. She turned, snuggling her head into the pillow. She wasn't particularly worried. Chad could do anything.

Chapter Seven

A soft tap on a nearby door brought Jennifer from a deep dreamless sleep. She forced her eyes open, dismayed to find herself in a room she didn't remember. Jennifer wasn't used to traveling. She was used to waking up in the same bed day after day. Yet for the past two days every time she had opened her eyes she was in a strange environment.

Another tap sounded on the door. "Ms. Chisholm?"

Max Taylor. The past few hours suddenly came back to her. Hastily sitting up, she ran her hand through her hair, trying to bring some semblance of order to it.

"Yes?"

The door opened and the man stepped through the doorway. "Your friend Tony has just called. Obviously you have not been aware of his regard for you.

He asked me to meet with him and to bring you with me."

"Oh." She slid off the bed and stood up, feeling around for her shoes with her feet. "He isn't coming out here?"

"No. We're to meet him in town."

After putting on her shoes Jennifer found her comb in her purse and quickly ran it through her hair. Then she followed Max out the door.

Once again she was escorted to the limousine, this time by her host. Silently they rode back to town.

Chad?

"?"

We're on our way to meet Tony. Are you with him?
"Yes."
I love you.

A feeling of love and warmth swept over her and she smiled. Who needed the words when she could feel so much expression from his emotions?

They eventually pulled up in front of a luxury high-rise condominium that overlooked a golf course. There was enough daylight left for Jennifer to appreciate the view before they went inside and rode up to the top floor in an elevator.

Max acted as though he'd been there before. He guided her down the hallway and paused in front of an unmarked door. Pressing a button, he stood back and waited.

Tony opened the door. Pulling Jennifer into his arms, he gave her a quick hug, then stepped back, still keeping his arm around her waist. "Come in, Max," he said politely. After he closed the door he leaned over and whispered in Jennifer's ear, "I'm sorry about all of this, honey. Tiger has been ready to take me apart limb by limb for the scare.''

"No problem," she said with a smile. "Where is he, by the way?" She glanced down the hallway.

"Straight ahead." He motioned for her to go ahead of him.

The hallway led into a large room that overlooked the city. Max was already standing there, waiting for them, when they walked in. So was Chad.

He strode over to Jennifer and looked down at her. "You okay?"

She nodded.

He glanced up. "If it's all the same to you two, we're leaving."

"Sure, no problem," Tony responded. "Max and I will probably be tied up for some time."

Max looked stunned to see the woman he had assumed belonged to Tony walking out with another man. Jennifer guessed that he was probably coming to the conclusion that he hadn't figured things out quite right, after all.

Chad didn't say anything all the way down in the elevator. Neither did Jennifer. When they reached the street, Jennifer looked up and said, "Now, what?"

He motioned to her car. When they got inside, he said, "I don't think it's a good idea to stay in town any longer. Would you mind driving home tonight?"

She smiled. "Not at all."

"I'm staying here. I've still got to find my car. Tony said he could probably find out from Max where it is."

He began to drive toward the Strip.

"Do you have any idea what's going on?"

"Tony's been filling me in, but there's no sense in getting you involved any more than you already are. That's why I want you to return home." He glanced at her. "Will you do that for me?"

She nodded. "Whatever you say."

"I'd looked forward to taking you out tonight. Maybe we can do it some other time."

"Maybe we can."

"Jennifer?"

She continued to stare straight ahead. "Yes?"

"Are you going to tell me what's wrong?"

"Just let down, I guess. I don't know."

"A lot of things have happened in the past forty-eight hours."

"Yes."

"You still aren't sure about me, either, are you?"

She glanced at him in surprise. "Of course I'm sure of you. I would trust you with my life."

"Thank you. But how are you going to feel about working with me now that you know who I am?"

"I'm not sure."

"We've got to take this one step at a time. Can you understand that?"

"Yes."

"Do you believe me when I tell you I love you?"

How could she not believe him when her mind was filled with his images, his feelings and thoughts? "I believe you."

He was quiet for many long minutes. "You need time to think it through."

She couldn't disagree. Jennifer no longer knew what to think or feel. She was confused, and being around

Chad at the moment was only contributing to the
problem.

Chad pulled up in front of the Lucky Lady and got
out of the car, leaving it running. She got out and
walked around to the driver's side. He stopped her
before she sat down. She stood by the door, leaning
against the car. He leaned over and kissed her very
softly on her lips. "Drive carefully."

"I will."

"Let me know when you get home."

"Okay."

"Tell Sam hello for me."

She groaned. She'd forgotten about Sam. "If he's
speaking to me by then."

Chad touched her cheek with his forefinger, tracing an imaginary line along her jaw, then up to her
lips. "I'll be back as soon as I can."

Jennifer suddenly remembered all the work waiting
for him when he returned. It was hard to remember
that when she'd left the office on Friday her boss had
been a distant and aloof employer to whom she gave
little thought after office hours. She shook her head,
bewildered at the changes that had come about so
quickly.

As though he could no longer help himself Chad
drew her closer and kissed her. She could feel his
heart's heavy rhythm in his chest. Jennifer realized
that he didn't want her to leave him. She got a brief
flash of them in bed together, and she could feel her
body beginning to respond.

Chad abruptly let go of her and stepped away, his
eyes refusing to meet hers, but not before his body, as
well as his thoughts, had given him away.

Jennifer slid into the car and closed the door.

"Don't forget, Sunshine. I want to know the minute you get home."

She nodded, refusing to look at him. One more look and she would wrap herself around him and beg to stay with him that night. Yet, that was what they were afraid of. What would happen once they made love to each other? Would it destroy the closeness they shared? Did they dare find out?

She knew Chad wasn't ready to test that part of their relationship. She wondered if he ever would be.

While Jennifer made the long, lonely drive back to Los Angeles, she finally recognized what she should have seen sooner. Chad had no intention of letting their relationship go any further. If he had, he would have told her who he was before now. She was beginning to understand why he had tried to talk her out of finding out who he was.

Chad had felt safe in the role he was playing in her life. He knew what she did in her time away from the office. He worked with her during the day, so was able to spend time with her.

If Chad had his way, they would continue their relationship as it now was, with her added knowledge of who he was.

Could she be content with a life like that? Not knowing the full physical intimacy of a relationship? Granted she hadn't been tempted to explore much before now, partly because she had never felt that pull with anyone. However, now that Chad had kissed her, had held her and had allowed her to discover how much he wanted her, Jennifer knew she was going to have difficulty coming to terms with not being able to fully share her life with him.

By the time Jennifer reached her apartment she was exhausted. She had only a few hours to sleep before it was time to get up and go to the office. There was no question but that she had to be there, now that she knew he wasn't going to be.

She barely got into the apartment before a flying ball of fur landed on her shoulder. "Sam! You scared me." He began to nuzzle her cheek and neck, telling her how miserable he'd been without her. He had begun to feel abandoned and was too pleased to see her to be upset.

Jennifer carried him into the bedroom along with her small bag. "I'm home, Chad."

The reply came back immediately. *"Thank God. Any problems?"*

"Not a one."

"Sam okay?"

"He seems fine. Very glad to see me, as a matter of fact."

"Probably did him good to be on his own for a while. He'll appreciate you more."

"Could be."

"Try to get some sleep now, Sunshine."

"When do you think you'll be back to the office?"

"I'll have to call you when I know something definite."

"Love you, Chad," she said sleepily as she climbed into bed and curled into her pillow.

"Sleep well, Sunshine. You've had a rough weekend."

When the alarm went off Monday morning, Jennifer had the curious sensation that she had dreamed her entire weekend. Was it really possible that C. W. Cameron was also her friend Chad?

By the time she had been at the office for a few hours the events of the weekend had been shoved to the back of her mind, and she found herself racing to stay abreast of the new paperwork and phone calls that came through with persistent regularity.

It was sometime after four o'clock and Jennifer had long since lost track of the number of calls she'd answered when the phone rang once again.

"Mr. Cameron's office."

"Ms. Chisholm?"

Jennifer's heart seemed to leap out of her chest. She had no trouble recognizing the deep voice on the other end. Nor did she miss the aloof tone and the name he had used. "Yes, Mr. Cameron?" She couldn't control the slight quiver in her voice.

"Is there anything happening that I need to know about?"

Funny you should ask, she thought dryly. "Several things came in the mail today that will prove helpful with some of your investigations." As she had done so often in the past years, Jennifer quickly summarized phone messages, information from the mail and interoffice communications. He gave her instructions, delegated some of the work, took down some numbers and told her he would be in touch.

"Uh, Mr. Cameron—?"

"Yes?" There was nothing but professional politeness in the tone.

"When do you expect to be in the office?"

"Hopefully the latter part of the week."

"Have they recovered your car?"

There was a moment of electrified silence, as though she had said something shockingly intimate. She waited, not knowing what else to do, but she got the definite impression that she was infringing on his privacy.

Jennifer had almost decided he wasn't going to respond at all when he said, "Yes. I have my car." A statement of fact, no more. He wasn't going to say when he got it, or where it had been, or if it had been damaged. And he had made it clear that it was none of her business.

"Oh. Well. I'm glad to hear it."

"Was there anything else?" he asked impatiently.

"No. I believe that was all," she said slowly.

"I'll check in with you in a day or two."

"Fine." Jennifer carefully put down the phone. The rest of the office was busy. No one had thought anything of the phone call she had just received. Just the normal communications between the boss and his assistant. That was the problem. It had been too normal. He had totally ignored everything that had happened over the weekend.

Jennifer spent the rest of the day concentrating on carrying out her employer's instructions. Carefully typing up his comments, she attached a sheet of paper to the front of new files she had set up, then placed them on the desks of the other two investigators.

By the time she was ready to leave the office, Jennifer was proud of what she had accomplished that day. Driving home she made the startling discovery that no doubt that was the reason Chad had reverted to the C. W. Cameron she knew. He valued her work as his assistant. He didn't want to cause anything to change that, even if he sacrificed a possibly closer relationship.

Once again, Sam seemed to be pleased to see her when she got home. She was glad someone was.

After dinner she tried to watch television, but couldn't keep her attention focused long enough to follow what was happening.

Finally, she could stand the silence no longer. "Chad?" She waited a few moments but got no response. "Chad. Can you hear me?" Still no answer. Again, this was nothing new. For the past six months she had not communicated with him. He was making it clear to her. The only reason he had contacted her on Friday was because he had no other recourse if he wanted to get out alive. She had served her purpose.

Jennifer didn't even realize she was crying until the tears began to drip off her cheeks. Nothing had really changed since last Friday. And yet, everything had changed. Jennifer had been given a glimpse of what her life could be with the man she loved. She also knew that he loved her. He hadn't been able to conceal his feelings from her.

But C. W. Cameron had made the decision not to do anything about his feelings. And he expected her to accept his decision.

During the coming weeks Jennifer tried. She put Chad out of her mind every time something reminded her of him. She put everything about her weekend in Las Vegas to the back of her mind, determined to wait until the pain was less before allowing herself to enjoy the few memories she had of being with him.

C. W. Cameron followed the same schedule as he had before. He spent a few days in the office, catching up on paperwork, then was gone again. Never by word, look or action did he give her any indication that he saw her as anything but his assistant. He treated her with aloof courtesy and distant kindness.

Jennifer wasn't at all sure she was going to be able to survive his courtesy and kindness. As the weeks went by, she felt less and less like eating and it began to show. Several of the women at work teased her about her new diet.

C. W. Cameron neither noticed nor cared.

Eventually her resistance dropped and she came down with the flu, missing several days work. He called once to see how she was feeling, but only as her boss concerned about her welfare.

During those days of fever and pain, of sleepless nights and drug-filled days, Jennifer realized that she had accepted his decision as final. Who did he think he was? Why did he have the right to step into her head and heart whenever he pleased, then blithely walk away when he became too uncomfortable with the situation?

By the time she woke up one morning, weak but clear-eyed, Jennifer knew that she was not going to give up without a fight. And the man she worked for had already taught her something about fighting, fair or otherwise. If one didn't work, she'd try the other.

She waited until she was able to get back to full production on the job, which took some time. Jennifer was disgusted at herself for allowing her body to become so weakened. She had more self-respect than that. In order to fill some of her lonely evenings she joined a health club and began to work out after she left the office. She met several people who came in regularly at the same time as she did and they began to visit back and forth while they worked on the machines.

Jennifer was pleased with her body's response. As she gained her weight back she began putting it on in all the right places. There had been nothing wrong with her body before, but now it looked even better.

She also discovered that she had much more energy. No longer did she drag home and fall on the couch exhausted after a day of hard work.

However, the biggest change was in her attitude to her employer.

"Good morning, Ms. Chisholm," he said one morning after having been out of the office for two weeks.

Her smile was warm and welcoming, filled with sparkle. "It's good to have you back," she said. Her tone was filled with such a loving quality that he glanced around to see if anyone else had heard her. No one seemed to be in the vicinity.

"Are these my messages?" he muttered, avoiding her gaze.

"Um-hmm," she said softly.

She watched with interest as a darker color spread over his tanned cheeks. "May I get you a cup of coffee?" she asked pleasantly.

His eyes darted to her in disbelief. In all the years they had worked together, she had never offered to bring him coffee before. He nodded abruptly. "Thank you," he said, striding into his own office.

She paused in the doorway of his office when she returned with his coffee. *I'm so glad you're back,* she said to him silently. *I've missed you.*

He never looked up, but she noticed his grip tightened on the pen he was holding. She set the cup down on his desk. "Do you need anything else?" she asked quietly.

He shook his head, refusing to look up.

Chad had heard her, she knew that. Whether he answered her or not, he had not tuned her out, which gave her an idea for another experiment.

She knew many things about this man, things she hadn't consciously realized. A person couldn't trade thoughts with another person for years without learning about them. Jennifer had also learned quite a lot about him the weekend they had spent in Las Vegas. That knowledge could be put to work to help her convince him that they deserved the chance to see if they could make a relationship work.

Jennifer had a vague glimmering of what she had in mind, but didn't have the knowledge to fulfill it. As soon as she got off work that night she went to the public library and checked out several books on sex. When she noticed the expression on the librarian's face, Jennifer just smiled and explained, "Research."

For the next couple of weeks Jennifer read several sex manuals, studied pictures and received a crash course in all the sensual arts. She found herself blushing more than once but reminded herself that all of this was perfectly normal and natural between two people who loved each other.

She loved Chad. She knew that Chad loved her.

Now all she had to do was to convince him to give their relationship a chance.

Chapter Eight

Jennifer planned her strategy carefully. For this to work at all, she wanted Chad in the same town, at least. So she had to wait until he returned from his latest trip.

In the meantime, she continued to treat him with warmth and friendliness whenever he called in, amused to note that he had become even more aloof with her efforts. Whether he was calling from out of town or was in the office, she was open and amiable with him.

The day he came in from the Midwest he looked tired and discouraged.

"How was your trip?"

"Rugged," was his only reply. He went into his office and sank down in his chair, staring at the papers in front of him with dismay.

"None of those are emergencies," she said, following him into the room. "May I make a suggestion?"

He glanced up at her warily, an expression to which she had grown accustomed during the past few months.

"Why don't you go on home?" she asked as though he had responded. "It's already after three. There's nothing here that can't wait until tomorrow to be dealt with, after you've had a good night's sleep."

He leaned his head wearily against the back of his chair. "That's the best idea I've heard in a while," he admitted.

"You've been working too hard."

His eyes met hers and she immediately knew what he was thinking. *"You know exactly why I've been working so hard."*

She was sure he wouldn't appreciate her acknowledging that she had picked up his statement. Instead, she said, "I have another suggestion. You might want to do what I do after a long, hard day."

"What's that?"

"I go home, fill my bathtub with warm water, pour myself a glass of wine, light a candle and sit there in the tub, sipping on the wine, and let my mind go blank. I try not to think of a thing. Just sit there and relax. It's amazing how much it helps. I sleep a lot better, too."

"I haven't been getting much sleep lately."

She steeled herself from responding that she knew. Because of her feelings for him, she had been able to tune into him more and more over the past few months. She knew how unhappy he was, how confused, and how determined he was not to do anything to cause her to quit her job and leave him entirely.

Chad had decided that half a loaf was better than nothing. He was wrong and she was determined to prove that to him. Half a loaf was a compromise that wasn't necessary or even wise. They deserved much more than that, and she was willing to go to great lengths to prove that to him.

He straightened in his chair. "I believe I may follow your suggestion." He glanced down at the stack of telephone messages in his hand. "You're sure these can wait until morning?"

"Positive."

He stood up. "Then I think I'll take your advice."

She stepped back so that he could pass her, but not far enough that he didn't have to brush by her as he passed. She felt him flinch.

Yes. He was vulnerable. But then, so was she. Love created vulnerability and it was all right, so long as the other partner didn't abuse it. That was what she intended to show Chad, if he would just give her a chance. Their deep feelings for each other were nothing to run away from, but something to run toward.

Jennifer made sure she left at five o'clock and went directly home to her apartment. There was no stopping at the health club tonight, no visiting with her friends. Instead, she did just what she suggested Chad do. She filled her bathtub with water, poured a small glass of wine, put a quiet instrumental recording to play on the stereo, lit a candle and, after stripping off her clothes, slowly lowered herself into the warm and soothing water.

Quieting her mind she began to tune in to Chad. He was quiet, as though asleep. That was all right. He needed his rest. She spent the next hour soaking and relaxing, and silently rehearsing.

By the time she had something to eat and was ready for bed, Jennifer was shaking with stage fright. So much depended on how she did this and how he responded.

She turned out the light and crawled into bed. Forcing her body and mind to relax, she began.

"Chad?"

"?"

"Are you asleep, love?"

She got a sense of drifting clouds and cool breezes. He was very relaxed, but she didn't think he was asleep.

"I was just lying here tonight, thinking of you, and decided to picture you here in bed with me."

She felt an electric vibration sizzle between them and knew beyond a doubt that she had his attention. She smiled to herself. "I see you lying next to me, your head on my pillow...."

She felt his energy surge, then retreat.

"I love to pretend that you're in bed with me, Chad. It makes my life less lonely. Are you tired of being alone, Chad?"

There was no response, but she knew she had his attention.

"If you were here I'd lean over and kiss you, very softly, on the lips. Your lips feel so good to me, Chad. I love their firmness, and the fullness of your bottom lip. If you were here, I would touch my tongue to its surface, and lazily taste your mouth."

She waited, but got no response.

"If you were here in my bed there would be no need for either of us to have on any clothes. I would want to feel your body pressed against mine."

"I?"

Jennifer smiled. "I wouldn't want any covers on us, either, and I would want a light on, so that I could see you...just as you could see me. I would want to touch you, explore you with my fingertips, to get to know your body as well as I know mine, to place my breasts against your chest and feel the soft downy curls on your chest brush against me."

"Jennifer!"

"Yes, Chad?" she responded.

"Would you cut that out?"

"What's wrong, Chad?"

"Not a thing. Not a damned thing."

"I'm sorry if I bothered you, love. I know how very tired you are and how much you need your rest."

Silence.

"I'm sure you're used to having a woman in bed with you. It doesn't mean a thing."

More silence.

"It's different with me, though. I've never wanted to go to bed with another man. Only you. Only you, Chad. I've been waiting years for you. I used to lie in bed at night and try to imagine what you looked like, but I never could. Now I know. I can see your muscular body, your strong, handsome features, I can feel your soft, thick hair through my fingers, and smell the tangy scent of your after-shave. I can feel your—"

"Why are you doing this?"

"What do you mean? Loving you?"

"Are you trying to make me lose my sanity?"

"Of course not. I love you, Chad."

"You don't know what you're talking about."

"Oh, but I do. You've given me a chance to come to terms with the Chad I grew up with, and the man I've known as my boss for five years. I no longer glamorize you, Chad. But that doesn't mean I love you any less."

"I'm not interested in a physical relationship with you."

"Oh? You really surprise me, Chad. As long as I've worked for you, I would never have guessed you preferred—"

"Damn it, Sunshine, you know better than that."

"You really had me fooled, you know. The way you kissed me, the way you touched and caressed me—"

"It's a good thing you aren't here right now, you know. I would show you my sexual preferences fast enough!"

She grinned. "Is that an offer? Give me your address and I'll be right there. Wait, I'll get a pencil." She lay there quietly, waiting for a response.

"Don't bother. I am not going to give you my address. You are not coming over here. You are going to leave me alone, do you understand me?"

"Very well. You come in very loud and clear. Can you hear me all right?"

She could feel his frustration, irritation and thwarted sexual desires all tangled in a whirlwind of emotion. The cool, unflappable C. W. Cameron might be able to hide behind that calm facade with everyone else, but he had given her an open pathway to his heart when she was too young to appreciate what he offered. Now there was no way he could close her out.

"Sunshine...I'm tired. I've had less than four hours' sleep in the past fifty-six hours. I'm beat. Will you please just go away and leave me alone?"

"Of course I will, love. Why don't you turn over on your stomach and relax. Just pretend that I'm there massaging the tense muscles in your back and shoulders. Feel my fingers glide over those muscles, and smooth away all of the aches. Feel my—"

"Jennifer Chisholm, that's enough!"

She lay there quietly in bed, grinning from ear to ear. After a few moments she heard, *"Sunshine?"*

Jennifer didn't answer.

After several more minutes went by, he said, *"Sunshine, I'm sorry. I don't want to hurt your feelings. I just want to be left alone, okay?"*

Jennifer turned over and snuggled into her pillows. Not bad for the first night's work.

She was on the phone when C. W. Cameron walked in the next morning. Without looking up at him she handed him three calls that had already come in for him, while she continued to speak into the phone.

When she hung up, Jennifer went back to the coffeepot and got two cups of coffee. Without saying anything, she placed one of them in front of him and sat down in the chair across from his desk.

He glanced up from the mail in front of him.

"Did you sleep all right last night?" she asked.

"No, thanks to you," he muttered.

Jennifer was delighted. That was the first time in the office that he had allowed their two separate lives to come together. It was a start.

Over the next several weeks Jennifer set up a loose schedule of contact with him. When he was out of town she would idly let him know when she went out with friends after work. He didn't need to know how many were in the group. If he thought she was on a date while she commented on what was happening around her, that was his choice.

Her purpose was to let him know that she wasn't wasting away without him; that she had a full and busy life and that she was happy with her environment. At the same time she let him know she missed him and wished he were there to share some of those good times with her.

He never responded.

Jennifer refused to become disheartened. She couldn't expect to break a twenty-year habit in a couple of months. Time was on her side. Actually, she knew that whether or not he would admit it, Chad was on her side, too.

It wasn't that he didn't love her. He was afraid of the commitment. Nothing new about that. Almost every magazine she picked up had an article or two about men and women who were afraid to make a commitment. She could understand and appreciate where they were coming from. If she hadn't grown up with Chad in her life, she would no doubt feel the same way. But because of Chad, her life was different.

Her commitment was made. That commitment had begun years ago when a teenage boy reached out to her in her loneliness and sorrow and tried to ease her pain.

Now it was her turn to reach out and ease his loneliness and sorrow.

He'd been back home from one of his trips two days when she sent him a message late one night. Jennifer was lying in bed and had been thinking about him. Focusing her thoughts to project to him, she said, "I wonder what it's like to sleep with someone, to actually share a bed. Are you used to sleeping with anyone, Chad?"

"What sort of crazy question is that?" was his immediate response.

Good. Many times he ignored her. She must have gotten under his skin with that one.

"That's not crazy. You're thirty-seven years old. I'm sure you haven't spent all that time in bed alone."

"You might be surprised."

"I lie here at night and pretend you're here with me, but since I'm not sure whether you're used to sleeping on your back or your stomach, or whether you'd curl up to my back or perhaps I'd curl up to yours..."

No response, but she felt his reaction, knew he was visualizing them together.

"I don't think I'd want to sleep in anything. Not with you here to keep me warm. You certainly do have a way of doing that. Every time you've kissed me my temperature has gone up a few notches. I can just imagine what it would be like for your hands to touch and explore me, to—"

She felt a very heated response, but no words.

"Good night, Chad. Pleasant dreams."

Actually Jennifer had discovered that her plan had somewhat backfired. She was finding that her sleep was filled with dreams of Chad and some of the books she had read came to life with her and Chad as eager participants.

She would wake up and find herself trembling, oftentimes aching with need. The mind and the imagination were the most erotic part of the body. Jennifer had absolutely no doubts on that subject.

And she wasn't going to be able to continue the torture she was putting them both through. After one particularly graphic evening, Jennifer ended up crawling into a cold shower for several minutes before going to sleep.

So much for trying to use their unique communication abilities to convince him they belonged together.

To make matters worse, once she managed to fall asleep she had slept so heavily she did not hear her alarm go off. Eventually Sam was able to get her awake by tromping up and down her back and meowing until she opened her eyes and saw the time. There was no way she could make it to work on time.

C. W. Cameron was already at his desk, with his cup of coffee, talking on the phone when she came in. That was the first time since she'd been working there that he had beat her in. Of course it was also the first morning she had been late.

He glanced up when she walked into her office, nodded and continued to talk while she hastily put her purse away and sat down. The mail was piled high on her desk and she automatically started sorting it, wishing she'd taken the time to swallow a couple of aspirin tablets before she left home.

Jennifer felt defeated. She had been so hopeful that in some way she would reach the stubborn, lovable, opinionated, tenderhearted, irritable, adorable man she loved. However, at the moment she was at a loss as to what to do. Nothing worked.

For the first time Jennifer faced the fact that she might need to quit her job. If she accepted that there would never be anything more between her and Chad than their working relationship, she wasn't sure she could continue.

Jennifer heard her employer hang up the phone but she didn't look up. When he suddenly spoke in front of her, she jumped.

"Leave that and get your purse."

The words were quiet but there was no doubt in her mind that he meant every word. She looked up at him, horrified. Granted, she had been considering leaving the agency, but she needed time to find other employment. Besides, how could he even consider firing her for being late, when it was the first time in all her years of working there?

His expression gave nothing away.

Are you firing me? she thought in a rush.

"No," was the equally quiet answer.

Jennifer got up and reached for her purse. He held out his hand as though for her to precede him. They paused at the receptionist's desk. "Ms. Chisholm and I will be out for the rest of the day. Please take our calls and tell whoever asks that we'll both be in on Monday."

The look of astonishment on the receptionist's face probably mirrored Jennifer's own expression. Chad had never before asked her to go anywhere with him. As a matter of fact, he hadn't asked now.

Trying to keep up with his long stride, she hurried beside him. When he noticed that she was almost running to keep up with him, he slowed his pace somewhat and politely took hold of her elbow. They stopped beside his car.

The sporty lines of his Nissan did not look in any way damaged, she thought as he unlocked the door, then held it open for her.

Jennifer settled in, made sure her safety belt was fastened and waited for him to explain where they were going. And waited. And waited.

When he pulled into the airport she glanced at him in alarm. "Are you going out of town again?"

He waited until she had gotten out of the car, made sure both doors were locked, then took her elbow once again, motioning her toward the terminal. "*We* are going out of town."

"But where?" She glanced down at the neat suit she wore. "I don't have anything to take with me."

"You won't need anything," he assured her blandly.

He kept walking past the ticket counters and toward the gates. They went through the security check in silence. When he stopped at one of the gates and gave his name she heard the announcement of the last call for the flight leaving for Las Vegas, Nevada.

Once again he ushered her through the gate and down the passageway to the plane. He gave their boarding passes to a smiling steward, who pointed out their seats. After making sure she was strapped in, he pulled some papers out of his inside coat pocket, unfolded them and began to read.

"Is Tony still having problems?"

He continued to read for a moment, then reluctantly raised his gaze to meet hers. "Not that I am aware of."

Clearly he wasn't in the mood to talk. Well, quite frankly, neither was she. Her head was pounding, her heart was racing, and she didn't understand what was going on.

They were already in the air before Jennifer realized this was her first flight. She'd been too confused and mystified to give it much thought.

Since Chad had given her the seat by the window, she spent most of her time looking out. Jennifer was determined not to give him the satisfaction of pleading to know what was going on. He paid her salary. If he decided to take her away from the office on one of their busiest days, she supposed that was his business.

Forcing her mind to quieten, Jennifer continued to stare out the window until she fell asleep. She woke up as they were making their final approach to land. Now she had plenty of time to worry about how well the pilot knew how to fly, if all the mechanics had been alert when they checked over the plane, and if anyone would think to notify her mother if something happened to her.

Chad obviously knew his way around an airport. Within minutes he had stopped to pick up the keys to a rental car and they were quickly outside.

The weather was much nicer in late October, Jennifer noted with something like relief. She started to make a comment along those lines to Chad when she caught a glimpse of his face. The aloof, thoughtful expression did not remind her of a man who was interested in passing the time by discussing the weather.

Jennifer waited to see where they were going.

Her first surprise was that they didn't go on the Strip. So they weren't going to see Tony, she decided. Her second surprise was when they parked near a very official building downtown and Chad escorted her into the courthouse and down the hall to the license bureau.

Her knees almost buckled when he explained to the clerk that they were there to get a marriage license.

Chapter Nine

The normal busy office sounds of the license bureau made a soothing background for Jennifer's thoughts, which could best be described as chaotic. She had assumed that the reason for their trip had something to do with the agency. By the time she could find some order to her thoughts, the clerk was asking rapid questions.

Jennifer answered them in a daze. Chad's composed answers further rattled her. After the money was handed over, Chad took the license and escorted her from the room. By the time they reached the hallway Jennifer had managed to find her tongue.

"Chad, wait!"

He looked down at her with no discernible expression and waited.

"We need to talk about this. I mean, you never—I didn't expect—We haven't—"

He held up his hand like a traffic cop at a school crossing. "You don't have to marry me if you don't want to, Jennifer. No one is forcing you. If you'd like, we can catch the next plane back to L.A. and—"

"I do want to marry you, it's just that—"

He took her arm and began propelling her down the corridor. "Then we shouldn't keep the judge waiting. He only has a few minutes between court hearings."

When she came out of the courthouse some time later, Jennifer felt as though she couldn't get enough air in her lungs. She felt as she had as a child when she had ridden the carousel—no matter how tightly she hung on, they were going around so fast she could scarcely catch her breath.

Once again they got into the car, only to drive a few short blocks. They pulled up in front of the Golden Nugget casino and hotel. The marble and gold trim glistened in the sun. She looked at Chad in total bewilderment. He assisted her from the car and handed the keys to the waiting attendant.

Once inside Jennifer stared around the lobby in awe. The place looked like her idea of a palace. Chad had gone over to the reservation desk, where he signed in and was handed a room key.

He took her arm and escorted her to the elevator.

When they reached their floor and started down the hallway Jennifer began to fully realize what had just happened. She and Chad were now married, and like any eager bridegroom he was rushing her to a hotel room.

Chad, rushing to get her in bed?

She glanced up at him but as usual could read nothing from his expression.

Chad? Not by a flicker of an eyelash did he betray that he heard her. Instead, he opened the door and motioned for her to precede him. The room was large and exquisitely decorated. Jennifer walked over to the window and peeked out. She heard the door close with a soft but definite thud and turned around.

Chad shoved the bolt through the door, then turned around. He reached up and began to loosen his tie as he slowly and deliberately paced toward her.

"Now, then. You may have to help refresh my memory as to what it is you want me to do to you." His coat came off and was tossed onto a chair. His tie soon followed and he started on the buttons of his shirt. "I believe the first thing was for us to be without any clothes, in the daylight, with no covers . . . so we could enjoy the sight of each other."

Jennifer felt a sudden need to retreat. Unfortunately her position by the windows precluded that, unless she wanted to be so undignified as to try to crawl out the window. With her luck, it was probably sealed. She put up her hands in a calming gesture. "W-wait a minute, Chad. I think we should talk about this."

"Talk? Haven't we done enough of that over the past . . . how many weeks has it been now? I can't remember when my sleep started to become interrupted with graphic descriptions of what you and I should do in bed together." He sat down on the side of the bed and quickly removed his socks and shoes. Standing once again, he unfastened his belt, unzipped his trousers and stepped out of them.

Jennifer could only stare at the man in front of her. Of course she had seen men stripped down to the barest of essentials. She'd been raised in Southern California, after all, and had spent much of her youth on the beach. But she had never seen C. W. Cameron in that condition. He could easily have caused quite a commotion on any beach.

Once stripped of the civilized clothing, Chad looked like a warrior. There wasn't an ounce of unwanted flesh on him. His broad shoulders and chest rippled with well-trained muscles. The navy-blue briefs he wore couldn't disguise his masculinity nor the well-developed muscles in his thighs.

Jennifer could only stare at him.

Barefoot, he padded over to her, reminiscent of some jungle cat silently stalking its prey. She took a deep breath and tried to release her tension along with the air. The exercise had worked in her aerobics class. She was willing to try anything at this point.

He paused in front of her, then began to systematically remove her clothes. Her hands came up to stop him.

"Is there something wrong?" he asked blandly.

"I just think we need to—"

"So do I. But it's more fun not to have clothes in the way."

"I mean, I think—"

"Ah, but this isn't the time to think, Sunshine. This is the time to feel, to enjoy, to experience." He tilted his head slightly, looking for the fastener on her skirt. He smiled when he found it and watched with enjoyment as her skirt fell to her ankles, leaving her standing in her teddy, hose and heels.

"Not bad at all," he commented. "I should have remembered my camera." He shrugged. "Can't remember everything, I suppose."

He took her by the hand and led her to the bed. Gently pushing, he lowered her to the bed and began to remove her hose.

Jennifer pushed his hand away. "I'll do it!" She removed her shoes and hose and she sat there, staring at Chad with something close to fear on her face.

Reaching behind her, he pulled down the covers to the bottom of the bed. Then he scooped her up and laid her on one of the pillows.

Chad stretched out beside her, turned on his side so that he faced her and propped himself up on his elbow.

"Now, then, it looks to me as if we still have on too many clothes, but I suppose they will take care of themselves."

Jennifer had always thought the teddy she wore to be feminine and dainty. She had never noticed how little the lace bodice actually concealed. There was more flesh than lace.

The same with the bottom half. Cut high on her thighs the silk and lace did more revealing than concealing. She must have leaped several inches when Chad rested his large hand on her abdomen.

"Why don't you just relax now? This is what you've been dreaming of and talking about for weeks now. Like Cinderella, your dreams are now coming true."

"Uh, Chad, before we go any further—"

He jackknifed up in bed. "You're absolutely right. It just isn't the same, is it? You kept insisting we would do this without any clothes." He reached over and slipped the tiny straps of her teddy off her shoulders and quickly pulled it down over her waist and thighs, knees and ankles.

Jennifer frantically felt around for the covers.

"No, no. None of that now," he said, smoothly sliding his briefs off his hips.

Jennifer quickly averted her eyes from his body. Her gaze met his and she saw the heated look of desire shining from his eyes. She blinked. He might be making a game of this, but there was no mistaking that his intentions were serious.

Closing her eyes, Jennifer tried to think, but it was no use. He was too close. She could feel his heated body brushing against her, smell that tangy after-shave that he wore, and when he leaned over and lightly touched his lips to her, she could still taste the flavor of his favorite mints.

This, then, was exactly what she had fantasized all these weeks. With her eyes still closed Jennifer tentatively reached out and touched his face, her palm resting on his cheek. He quickly turned his head and placed a kiss in her palm.

She slid her hand up through his hair. Jennifer loved the feel of his hair—the clean crispness that still had a faint scent of the herbal shampoo he used. Blindly she lifted her mouth to his. He accepted her offering with a gentleness that eased the constriction that had been in her chest since she had first awakened that morning.

This was Chad—Chad who had spent a lifetime teasing and provoking her, Chad who knew her better than anyone else in the world, Chad who had taught her so much—who was about to take the next step in her education.

Somehow his knee seemed to belong there between her thighs. It rested very comfortably there, and Jennifer became used to its solid weight pressing her gently into the soft mattress.

There was so much she wanted to learn about him. Jennifer began to trace the line of his shoulders and arms with her fingertips, barely grazing the surface. She felt a chill run over his skin where she had touched. She smiled.

Later her fingers tangled in the soft hair on his chest, and she explored the path of curls as they nestled enticingly around his nipples. Feeling bold and venturesome, Jennifer placed her lips on one of his nipples and felt the jolt to his body.

Following the path of hair on his chest, she noted that it narrowed at his waist and swirled around his navel. She touched her tongue lightly to the slight indentation there and once again felt his body respond.

She continued her exploration by running her fingertips down his thighs, feeling the hard muscles lightly covered by a dusting of blond hair. He had such a beautiful body. She felt as though she had been invited to feast at a sumptuous banquet and wasn't sure where to start.

Before she could decide, Chad seemed to have other ideas. He pulled her back down beside him and he began to kiss her—long, mind-drugging, consciousness-removing kisses. No longer tentative, they made a claim on her, coaxing and beguiling her to follow his lead.

Jennifer idly noted that her arms were wrapped tightly around his neck, holding him as securely as he held her. Her hands could not stay still. They roamed restlessly across his broad shoulders, following the slight indentation of his spine as it made its way down his back. He felt wonderful.

When Chad's mouth finally slipped away from hers, Jennifer drew in some much needed air. She felt as though she were about to faint from excitement. Then she discovered why his mouth had slowly made a path of kisses down her neck. He was inching closer to her breast, which was cupped in his large hand.

His tongue darted out and touched the pink tip, causing it to contract and harden. Then his lips slowly surrounded it. Jennifer had never felt such a sensation in her life. Her whole body seemed somehow to be connected with that small, dainty tip. She felt an inner tugging, deep inside, as though a dam had been opened, and moist, hot sensations leaped and swirled in her depths. Her bones and muscles seemed to liquefy, and she had a sudden picture of herself, lying on the bed beside Chad, turned into melted honey.

Taking his time, Chad eventually moved slightly so that his mouth could taste the other breast. His fingers lightly played with the tip of the one he'd just abandoned as though to soothe it while he was gone.

Jennifer discovered she was gasping as though there weren't enough oxygen in the room. Her skin seemed to have a life all its own as it rippled under his touch.

Time and place seemed to disappear. They had drifted into an uncharted world with no landmarks for Jennifer to grasp and identify. Surprisingly enough, she wasn't afraid because Chad was right there with

her, every step of the way. He led her, yet he never
rushed. He introduced her to new sensations, but
never coerced. And by the time he shifted his weight
so that he was above her, Chad filled her vision and
her mind with his presence.

Here was the culmination of everything she had
hoped for, everything she had dreamed of. Chad was
offering his love, his very being to her.

She accepted his gift as she accepted his body, so
that they could share this ultimate union—the one final but necessary step to complete all that they were to
each other.

Jennifer realized that they had shared this ecstasy
before, many times—the intermingling of their
thoughts and feelings and their love. Only now they
were allowing their bodies to express themselves in a
similar fashion.

The act of love. What an appropriate name for such
a beautiful commingling of bodies, minds and spirits.
To be able to express óneself in this most intimate of
ways seemed to be the ultimate blessing given to human beings. They became one in the most literal sense
of the word; whole, complete and perfect in their union.

Jennifer didn't remember falling asleep, but when
she woke up hours later the room was dark and the
covers were pulled up around them both.

She lay in the curl of Chad's body, while his arm
and leg effectively held her closely to his side. Well,
that answered another question about how they would
sleep, Jennifer decided with a grin.

There was no reason to get up, although she recognized that she was a little hungry. Chad slept heavily
beside her. Her mind flitted back over the past several

hours. She still couldn't believe it. She and Chad were married. She was now Jennifer Cameron. Mrs. C. W. Cameron.

Of course Chad wasn't his real name. She had seen his legal signature many times. Charles Winston Cameron. He would always be Chad to her.

Jennifer wondered what all of this would mean when they returned to Los Angeles. They had never talked about marriage before. She had no idea where he lived, nor if he had family living. She knew his father was dead. Did he have any brothers or sisters?

Her eyes widened when she thought about her mother. Although they talked on the phone on a regular basis, she didn't see her mother as often as she'd like. Now she was going to have to come up with some way to explain her sudden marriage to her boss.

That was going to take some fast talking, she knew. Her mother had been full of questions when Jennifer was first promoted, no doubt hoping that something might come of the closer association with an eligible bachelor. Jennifer had wasted no time in setting her mother straight. Her description of C. W. Cameron had caused them some hilarious moments.

Now she had to find a way to explain to her mother. She wondered if she could start out with, "Say, Mom, do you remember my invisible friend, Chad, I used to have when I was a child? Well, I married him."

Somehow that didn't have the right ring to it. How about, "Say, Mom. A funny thing happened at the office the other day. I looked up at cool, aloof Mr. Cameron and fell madly in love with him. He admitted he felt the same way, so we—"

Nope. That didn't really get it, either.

Maybe—, "Mom, I met this tall, good-looking stranger one weekend when I was in Las Vegas. No, Mom, I don't go to Las Vegas as a rule. Honest, Mom, I'd never been there before in my life. Really, Mom—" So much for that idea. She'd never get past the first sentence.

"You know, Mom, love is a funny thing. You never know when it's going to hit you. It's kind of like a disease. That's it, an incurable disease. And you look at a person and see them totally different. Well, one morning when I went to work I looked up and there was Mr. Cameron and I discovered the love of my life."

The trouble with anything she might say was that no matter how she explained that she had suddenly married her boss she knew her mother would immediately suspect Jennifer was on drugs.

She sighed. No doubt she'd come up with something when the time came. Her eyes drifted shut. She really was tired. She couldn't remember the last good night's sleep she'd had. Jennifer smiled, thinking of the nights she had pretended that Chad was curled up to her back, holding her close. Her imagination hadn't been able to come close to provoking this sense of total bliss. . . .

The next time Jennifer awoke, she was more aware of Chad's touch than anything else. He must have awakened and found her in his arms. His mouth seemed to be quickly memorizing her body and his hands were doing things to her that must be banned in Boston.

Jennifer responded with the newfound knowledge she'd discovered about herself—she enjoyed, very much, the physical side of their relationship. And she was learning something new all the time.

For the next two and a half days the newlyweds didn't leave their room. Food was delivered and quickly consumed. When they weren't eating or sharing a friendly shower, they were in bed—either asleep or making love.

There was very little conversation that weekend.

Chapter Ten

All good things have to end sometime. Jennifer had heard that phrase all of her life, but to tell the truth, she'd never given it much thought. Since there hadn't been many good things that had happened to Jennifer, she'd never learned how and when they ended.

Her brief honeymoon was different. If she could have wrapped the memories and taken them home with her, she would have, to savor and enjoy over and over down through the years. Unfortunately, life didn't work that way.

They caught an evening flight back to Los Angeles. Jennifer had long since let go of her need to ask questions. She was quite content to follow Chad's lead at the moment. She'd found nothing to complain about so far in his plans. Adopting a wait-and-see attitude was not only different for her, but fun as well.

C. W. Cameron had never been one for small talk, so she wasn't surprised that he had little to say to her now. He could no longer hide the possessive gleam in his eye when he looked at her. She rather liked that possessive gleam. Jennifer had a hunch that if she took the time to look in a mirror she'd see a similar gleam looking back at her.

What a weekend. Chad had requested toothbrushes—everything else had been provided by the hotel when they got there. Obviously clothes had not been a problem. They merely put on what they had worn on Friday. Luckily Jennifer had had the foresight to hang up their clothes so that they didn't look too wrinkled.

Her hair had been something of a problem. Without a drier it had dried naturally, allowing the natural wave to have its way. She had managed to subdue it with some pins she had in her purse. Anyone looking at the two of them in their sober suits would assume they were business associates returning from a meeting.

And what a meeting that had been!

Jennifer glanced down at her bare hands. He hadn't given her a ring. When had he had time to get one? She wasn't sure when he'd made up his mind to marry her, but had a hunch it was during the last sleepless night they had both spent when she'd been so explicit in her fantasies.

He had an amazing memory, come to that. He had done everything she had ever suggested in her wildest fantasies, plus some things she had never read about in Masters and Johnson. No wonder he could say he hadn't slept with very many women. When did they have time to sleep?

Jennifer glanced at Chad from the corner of her eye and noted a slight grimness around his mouth. Perhaps it was normally there but she hadn't noticed it during the past two days. His lips had been anything but grim.

After arriving back in Los Angeles Chad guided her to where they had left the car. His experience at airports and in airport parking lots was understandable—and welcome.

Jennifer was curious to know where he intended them to spend the night. She would need to go home and feed Sam. Poor Sam. She'd also need clothes for work tomorrow. However, he might prefer staying at his place. She would wait and see what he suggested.

However, his suggestion was the last thing she expected.

They pulled into the office parking lot and Chad parked next to her car. For the first time since they left Las Vegas he turned around and looked at her fully. Jennifer felt a sudden premonition that she wasn't going to like what he had to say.

She didn't.

"I'm going out of town early in the morning. I need to go home and pack. I should be back by the end of the week. That should give us time to decide what to do about our marriage."

She stared at him, stricken by the lack of any emotion in his voice. "What do you mean, what we should do about our marriage?"

Chad ran his hand through his hair. "This isn't really the time to discuss it."

"I agree," she said. "We should have discussed it before we got married. However, we didn't, so it looks like now is the time."

Chad leaned his arms on the steering wheel and rested his chin on them. She'd never noticed his profile before. The clean, strong lines intrigued her. This man of the many different personalities intrigued her. If she ever figured him out, she would probably be able to write a book about him. There was no one else around like him.

"You made me angry," he finally admitted to the windshield.

She thought about that for a moment. "So you married me as punishment?" she asked.

"You have been slowly driving me out of my mind for months with your lovemaking fantasies. I couldn't take them anymore."

Jennifer didn't know what to say. She sat there, staring at him.

"You've been a part of my life for too long, Sunshine. I couldn't take advantage of you. I knew exactly how you felt about sex and lovemaking. And why not? I helped to instill those values in you. Yet you had pushed me past my limit of tolerance. So I married you. I didn't feel I had a choice."

"You married me so you wouldn't feel guilty about making love to me?"

"Yes."

"I see."

"But I don't like being manipulated. Nobody does. You took something special that we shared, something so unique that I have never been able to explain it in words, and used it against me. Okay. You won.

I'm not sure what it was you wanted but if it was to make me want you so much that I never seemed to be able to get over aching for you, then you accomplished what you set out to do.''

He never looked at her. His entire conversation was directed to the windshield in front of him. She might not even have been in the car with him for all the notice he gave her.

''I decided to solve both our problems. By marrying you, I felt it was acceptable for me to make love to you, something you have obviously been determined to have happen.''

''But you don't want to be married to me.''

For the first time he looked around at her. ''If you would stop and think about it, I don't lead a life that is conducive to marital harmony. I'm gone more often than I'm here. I put in long hours at the office. I don't have the time nor the energy to work on a relationship. . . with you, or anyone else.''

As far as that was concerned, Jennifer hadn't given much thought to marriage, either. She enjoyed her life, her freedom and her ability to do whatever she wanted.

''Why does marriage have to change anything?'' she asked in what she hoped was a reasonable tone of voice.

''It just does, that's all.''

''It doesn't have to. Look at it this way. Nothing that we like about our lives has to change. You travel, I have my time to myself. But when you're home, we're together. What's wrong with that?''

He thought about her suggestion for a few moments. ''What about children?''

"You made very sure that we were protected this weekend. I think that's a choice we can make. Who knows? Maybe you'll get tired of traveling one of these days. Stranger things have happened, you know."

He shook his head. "I think we need some time to think about it. I'll see you later on this week."

So she was dismissed, just like that. Jennifer got out of his car with all the dignity she could muster. Marriage ceremony or not, she felt that she had just participated in a wild, weekend fling that he regretted now that it was over.

She wasn't sure how she felt at this point. There was a blessed numbness that seemed to have wrapped around her.

Without saying another word, she got into her car and drove away.

This time Sam didn't let her off the hook for going away and leaving him alone. He had run out of food, although there was still some water left. As far as that went, he could go on a diet and it wouldn't hurt him any.

But his angry greeting seemed to be all Jennifer needed. She closed the door of the apartment, looking around to see that nothing had changed. Not a thing. Only her. She had changed and she knew she would never be the same again.

Chad had been right. She had exerted pressure on him, unfair pressure, to get him to acknowledge how he felt about her. He had acknowledged it, all right. Although he had wanted her physically, he resented her as well. Resented her for using his feelings for her to get what she wanted.

She couldn't blame him, really. She could remember several instances in the past when he had bullied her into doing something she didn't particularly want to do. She had resented his interference.

Now he felt the same way toward her.

Jennifer lay awake that night for hours, staring at the ceiling, thinking of everything that had happened. She had been on an emotional roller coaster these past few days. She tried to decide her best course of action, but nothing seemed suitable.

She was married to the man of her dreams, to her very secret lover, and he felt that she had trapped him into the relationship. In the small hours of the morning, Jennifer took a long, hard look at what she had done and was forced to agree with him.

The question was, what could she do about it now?

When Jennifer walked into the office Monday morning nothing had changed. Everyone greeted her as they always did, her desk was stacked with mail, as it always was, and the phone was ringing. Nothing new.

Only she was different. She wasn't the same woman who had walked out Friday morning, mystified as to why her employer had told her to leave with him.

If he wanted to punish her for what she had done, he could have found nothing more fitting than to give her a glimpse of what life would be like living with him, then to close the door.

She looked into his office. His out box was overflowing. He must have put in several hours of work before she arrived last Friday. Going into his office was difficult. It was so much a part of him and reflected his personality—organized, neat—and like her, waiting for his return.

By noon Jennifer knew she would have to talk to someone or go crazy. She called her mother and suggested dinner that night. Her mother was delighted.

"Mom, I have something to tell you that I know you're going to find hard to believe," Jennifer said that evening, over coffee.

They had enjoyed a leisurely meal at one of her favorite restaurants near where her mother lived.

Her mother smiled. "Nothing you could say would ever surprise me, Jennie. I have never known anyone with an imagination such as yours. I can remember so many of your stories—" She laughed. "But go ahead, dear." She patted Jennifer's hand. "Tell me."

Great. With a leadoff like that, Jennifer knew her mother would think she had made everything up.

"Mom. Some of this I have known for a long time. Some of it I've slowly found out over the past few months. Please bear with me, because I'd like to take it in sequence."

Jennifer paused, gathered her thoughts. "Do you remember the accident that caused Daddy's death, when two boys..." She began the story. She took her time, telling her the little bit that she could remember from that time. Then she told her all that Tony had shared.

Finally she told her mother how Chad had been able to mentally communicate with her.

Her mother's eyes had grown larger with the telling. But she had not interrupted Jennifer. Not once.

Jennifer continued the story through her growing-up years, and how she and Chad had finally lost touch with each other. Or so she thought.

"A couple of months ago I accidentally found out who Chad was."

Her mother looked confused. "I thought you said you knew. He was the young boy who—"

"No, I mean who he is now."

A tiny crease appeared between her mother's brows. "And who is that, my dear?"

"My boss, C. W. Cameron."

Her mother stared at her in astonishment. "I don't believe it. That cold, callous, arrogant man—"

Jennifer grinned at the description her mother had gained from the many stories Jennifer had told her. "That's right, Mom. The same man."

"But you describe Chad as so warm and loving, so very caring."

"He is."

"How could one man be so different?"

"I've given considerable thought to that over the past few months. I believe that the Chad I knew felt free to express himself. There were no conditions placed on him, no expectations of a certain behavior, no need to prove anything to anyone. In the fullest sense of the word, he allowed his inner self, his very essence, to unfurl and grow without hindrance."

Jennifer leaned back in her chair and sipped on her coffee. "I don't know the whole story, but from what I have learned through the office grapevine, Chad's father was a ruthless sort of a man, very demanding, who insisted on perfection from everyone around him, and considered that he gave nothing but the best, as well." She set her cup down and idly toyed with the handle. "I've tried to picture what Chad's young life was like. I have no idea who else was in his family, but obviously his father expected him to follow in his footsteps. So Chad did. He bottled all of his softer emotions away so that nobody ever saw them."

"Except you," her mother murmured.

They sat there quietly together, thinking about the young Chad Cameron and the conflicts he must have had to master.

"The only real coincidence in the story is that I went to work for Chad's company. That isn't as much of a coincidence as you might think, since the secretarial school I attended was only a few blocks away and the agency was always looking for stenographers. I understand the Camerons, both father and son, were difficult to work for, and they had a high turnover of personnel."

"I thought you said that changed, after you came to work."

"It did, and I'm beginning to understand why. Somehow I became a buffer between Chad and the rest of the staff. I was the one who caught most of the flak, and I could take it. At least most of the time. As he became accustomed to working with me, he calmed down."

"It probably didn't hurt that you were his childhood friend."

Jennifer grinned. "Good point. I hadn't really thought about that. But maybe he knew me so well he didn't need to intimidate or browbeat me into doing what needed to be done."

"As I recall, he did enough of that anyway."

"I know. I often look back and wonder why I stayed with him. He used to make me so angry!"

"I never could understand that, myself. You used to call me in tears. Whenever I suggested you quit, you said you didn't want to admit he could get the best of you."

They looked at each other. "I still don't, Mom, which brings us to the rest of the story, as they say."

"You mean, there's more? You know, this beats some of the wildest stories you used to tell as a child. I don't think even you have imagination enough to have dreamed up all of this."

"Just wait, Mom. You haven't heard everything. You see, last Friday, my boss, Mr. C. W. Cameron, and I flew to Las Vegas and were married."

Jennifer's mother looked as though a bucket of ice water had just been tossed in her face. She sat there staring at her daughter, her mouth slightly open.

Jennifer nodded. "I know, Mom. Unbelievable."

"But you never hinted, never by a word, that anything was going on between you."

"There wasn't, at least not in the way you mean. You see once I found out that Chad and C.W. were one and the same, I began to spot the similarities. He tried his best to keep the two personalities separate. But I started treating him differently in the office. I talked to him the same way we mentally communicated—easy, casually, and with a great deal of warmth."

"What did the people in the office think about your change?"

"Oh, they didn't see it. People avoid him as much as possible in the office, so no one would stick her head in my office whenever he was in town. It's almost comical, really, the lengths people will go to to avoid him.''

"Well, what do they think now? Were they surprised to hear you're married to him?''

"Nobody knows.''

"Aahh. That makes sense. He wants to keep it a secret.''

"I have no idea what Chad wants, Mom. That's why I'm here telling you all of this. You see, he brought me back from Las Vegas after the most beautiful weekend, dropped me off at my car, told me he would be out of town all this week and he'd see me later.''

Jennifer's mother choked slightly on her water. Coughing, she waved away her daughter's help and eventually exclaimed, "The man has to be the most insensitive, irritating, boorish oaf I've ever heard of.''

"That's one explanation. There might be others.''

"Name one.''

"I was a little underhanded in my attempts to get him to spend more time with me.''

"In what way?''

"Let's just say that I used our unique manner of communication to help him visualize some of the delightful ways we could spend our evenings, and nights, together.''

"Jennifer Chisholm! You didn't!''

"I'm afraid so, Mom. I can't say that I'm particularly pleased with my tactics, but they did provide some results. Not exactly what I had in mind, though.''

"Are you saying you were hoping for an affair with him?"

The way her mother said that caused Jennifer to bite her lip to keep from smiling. Her mother's words were spoken in a tone that indicated how hard she was trying to make an affair seem like an everyday occurrence. But Jennifer knew for a fact that her mother had shown no interest in a man since she'd lost her husband.

"I'm not sure what I was hoping for, to be honest. I hadn't given any long-range thought to what effect I was having on him and how he would handle it."

Her mother sat back and studied her for a moment in silence. Then she smiled. "So you're married, are you?"

She nodded. "It looks that way, doesn't it?"

"What do you intend to do about it?"

"Fight for my marriage. What else?"

"Do you have any idea how?"

"No. I'm open to suggestions."

Jennifer's mother gathered up her purse and stood up. "Well, let's go home and see what we can do. At least you can't say you don't know the man. Surely with all that knowledge, you can figure out what to do to convince him the two of you belong together."

Jennifer followed her mother from the restaurant, a sense of expectancy invading her being. Somehow, someway, she had to convince C. W. Cameron that he had made the best decision in his life when he married her.

Chapter Eleven

Chad?"

"?"

"Are you awake?"

"*Just barely. What is it?*"

Jennifer lay on her side in bed, Sam sprawled out beside her. She had been in bed for almost an hour, since eleven, and was unable to sleep.

"Nothing, really. I was just thinking of you, wondering if you were all right."

"*Are you?*"

She felt his concern. So he had been thinking of her. Three days had gone by since she had seen him. And three nights. Jennifer had discovered how quickly a person can become used to new experiences. She missed Chad in bed with her, holding her, loving her. She missed his presence.

"I miss you," she responded.

"I've got the same problem," he admitted.

"I had no idea being together could be so wonderful."

He didn't say anything for a moment. Then he said, *"I was afraid we might have overdone it a little. We were quite active for it to be your first exposure."*

"Let's just say that I haven't been in the mood to go to the club and work out since we got home." After a few moments of silence, she said, "Do you know yet when you'll be back?"

"No."

She tried for whimsical humor. "You can't stay gone forever, you know. Sooner or later you have to come home."

"I know."

"But you aren't looking forward to it," she offered gently.

"It isn't that. I just feel so—confused, somehow. I can't seem to get my life into any understandable order. All these years I've been in control of my life. Now . . . now I don't know what to think, what to do, how to evaluate what's happening."

"That's because feelings and emotions aren't that definable. We can't push them into little compartments and expect them to stay there. That's part of being human."

"If all this confusion is part of being human, I think I'll pass."

"And go back to being a robot?"

"Is that what I am?"

"I think that's what you've tried to be. Thank God, it didn't work."

They were quiet for several moments. At least he was communicating with her again, Jennifer was pleased to note. She was afraid their marriage had caused him to push that part of their relationship out of his life.

"Sunshine?"

She smiled at the familiar nickname. "Yes?"

"What are you wearing?"

She glanced down and grinned. "My flannel pajamas with the feet in them."

"?"

"Well, nobody's ever seen me in them but Sam."

"Have you ever thought about an electric blanket?"

"I have one. In fact, I generally keep it set close to broil."

"You didn't get cold while we were in Vegas."

"How could I, with almost two hundred pounds of brawn draped around me."

"One hundred eighty."

"Oh. Well, what's a few pounds here and there?"

"Sunshine?"

"Yes?"

"I know I wasn't fair to you last weekend."

"In what way?"

"I didn't give you a choice."

"Sure you did. Remember, you stopped me in the hallway and asked if—"

"You know what I mean. I never really asked if you wanted to marry me."

"I have never wanted to marry anyone else."

"But I know what you think of C. W. Cameron."

"If I'd had any idea all these years that my boss could read my mind," she teased, "would I have been embarrassed. I called you some pretty rotten names."

"After giving them some thought, most of the time I agreed with you."

"What about the times you didn't agree with me?"

"I waited to see if you were going to simmer down. No one would believe the temper you've got, just to see you and work around you. You keep it very well hidden."

"You've got the same abilities, you know."

"I'm afraid not. My temper seems to be legendary."

"I don't mean that. You have the ability to hide your softer side, the Chad side that I love so much, from the outside world."

"There isn't much call for him in the business world, I'm afraid."

"Perhaps not. But you don't have to think about business all the time. There are times for tenderness and love, for caring and comforting."

"Not in my life."

"Of course in your life. You've done it for years. With me."

"Oh, that."

"Yes, that."

"But you're different."

"No. *You* are different when you're with me. But you don't seem to want to show it except in these conversations—and last weekend."

"You mean I wasn't C. W. Cameron last weekend?"

"You were all that you could be, Chad. All your marvelous attributes and your loving disposition revealed themselves. If you gave yourself a chance, you could be that way more often."

"If we spent all of our time together like that, the office would fall apart."

"I don't mean in bed. I mean relaxed, and friendly. We could joke and talk in the office the same way we did over dinner, or in the shower."

"Now that might prove very interesting. I wonder what the staff would think?"

"You know what I mean. Don't be afraid to let your emotions show, Chad. There's nothing to be afraid of."

He was quiet for several minutes. Then he said, *"I'm not sure I could ever do that, Sunshine."*

"It doesn't matter to me, Chad, because I already know they're there. But it might make a difference for you."

After a while, he said, *"Good night, Sunshine."*

"Good night, Chad."

She felt his love wrap around her and she smiled as she drifted off to sleep.

By ten o'clock Friday morning the office was in an uproar. Phones were ringing, people were having trouble with office equipment, and Jennifer was ready to storm out screaming.

Part of her problem was that she hadn't heard any more from Chad. She hesitated to be the one who always contacted him, so she had waited, but there had been nothing. That had never bothered her in the past, but things were different now. Or at least she hoped so.

Was he getting used to the idea that he now had a wife to return to?

The office intercom buzzed and when Jennifer answered the receptionist asked, "Is there by any chance a full moon?"

Jennifer laughed. "I'm not sure. Why?"

"Oh, everything's so crazy around here. Some of the questions I've been getting. I think some people think this office is run like Mike Hammer's."

Jennifer grinned. "We should be so lucky."

"Well, actually, Mr. Cameron isn't bad, if he'd just unbend a little." There was a buzz in the background. "Got another call. See ya."

Jennifer shook her head, smiling. She wondered if Chad would like being compared with Mike Hammer? If only people knew how tedious investigative work was. Except for a few unusual incidents like the time when Chad got abandoned in a hunting cabin in southern Utah, it could be rather boring.   She was smiling when she answered the phone.

"Mr. Cameron's office. May I help you?"

"Ms. Chisholm?" She recognized his voice immediately. So. No matter what he might communicate to her privately, he was still going to be formal around the office.

Maybe it *was* a full moon, because she replied, "No, I'm sorry. Ms. Chisholm is no longer employed by this firm." She paused a beat and said in her most honeyed tones, "This is Mrs. Cameron, Mrs. Charles Winston Cameron. May I help you?"

The long distance wires hummed while she waited for a reply. "Jennifer?" he finally asked.

"Yes?" She kept her voice pleasant and very businesslike.

"Are you going by that name now?"

"I have a piece of paper, duly recorded, stating that to be my correct and legal name."

"I know. I just didn't realize you'd be using it around the office."

"I was forced to do so, sir, in order to stop all those nasty, vicious rumors going around about you."

"What rumors?"

"Those slurs on your manhood, sir. There has been talk about the possibility you weren't interested in women."

"What?" he yelped.

"Don't worry, sir," she said in a soothing voice. "I have certainly put paid to any such nonsensical remarks. I explained, in great and explicit detail, that after two and a half days of being locked up in a bedroom with you, there was no doubt in my mind as to your manhood." She paused for a couple of seconds and added, "Now, then, sir. How may I help you this morning?"

Jennifer was fascinated to discover that sometimes C. W. Cameron had trouble getting words out. He stumbled once or twice, cleared his throat and managed to say something that sounded like, "You're kidding, of course."

"You mean you don't want me to defend your reputation, sir?"

"You didn't really tell everyone about last weekend, did you?"

"It's nothing to be ashamed of, sir. You should be very proud of yourself. How many thirty-seven-year-old men could—"

"Jennifer!"

"Yes, sir?"

"Would you please stop calling me 'sir.'"

"Yes—What do you want me to call you?"

"What have you called me in the past?"

"Mr. Cameron. However, I refuse to call the man I sleep with by his last name. It smacks of class discrimination during the Edwardian era." She glanced over at his stack of calls. "Was there some particular reason you called? I can read you your messages or summarize the mail, whatever you wish."

Jennifer had the distinct impression that Chad was silently counting to himself. Yes, that was exactly what she picked up on him. So far he had passed twenty and was still climbing. Perhaps that was how he kept that ironclad control of his. He must be a mathematical wizard by now.

"Yes. I'd like to know what mail I have and any urgent messages."

For the next several minutes their conversation was filled with business. He gave her instructions for the other investigators, including the information that he would not be home for another week.

"I thought you said you'd be home in a few days."

"I had planned to. However, I ran into some problems that have caused me to change my plans."

"I see." As a secretary, it made very little difference to her whether he was there or not. She could take instructions in person or by phone. As a wife, it made a considerable amount of difference. Particularly since she was a new wife. A brand-new wife. With no husband in evidence.

Jennifer couldn't help but wonder if his delay had more to do with their new marital relationship than business problems, but she refused to ask. As she had pointed out to him before, he had to come home sometime.

Suddenly C. W. Cameron said something so astounding, she almost dropped the phone. He asked her a personal question. "What are your plans for the weekend?"

In all the years she'd worked for him, he'd never asked such a question. She had finally decided that as far as her employer was concerned she went up in a puff of smoke every Friday afternoon at five, only to reappear bright and early each Monday morning.

Maybe there was hope for them yet.

She didn't want to tell him that she had kept the weekend free just in case he were in town. Thinking quickly, she said, "Oh, I'll probably spend the weekend with Mother. She's always trying to get me to come visit."

"How is your mother?"

She stared at the phone as though he'd slipped into a foreign language. "Mom's fine. I had dinner with her Monday night."

"Oh."

She waited for him to say something else. She sure didn't know how to conduct this particular conversation.

"Did you tell her about us?"

"Yes."

"What did she say?"

"She wondered if she was going to have an invisible son-in-law and if her grandchildren would also carry the curse of invisibility."

"I'm looking forward to meeting her."

"She's looking forward to meeting you, too."

There was another pause. "I, uh, need to get to work. I'll talk with you next week."

"Fine. Is there anything else?"

She waited. Finally, in a low voice, he said, "I miss you, Sunshine."

Jennifer had difficulty concentrating on her work for the rest of the day.

"Definitely a good sign," her mother commented that evening. Jennifer and Sam had traveled out to Oceanside. Jennifer and her mother sat in front of the small fireplace, watching the flames while Sam checked out the place. A cat can't be too careful about the places he inhabits. Periodically he would leap up in Jennifer's lap and touch his nose to hers. Satisfied that she was behaving, he would jump down and continue his reconnaissance.

"I thought so," Jennifer agreed. "I don't think Chad consciously chose such a dramatic split in his personality. Little by little, through various circumstances and experiences, he worked out a pattern of survival."

"You know what I really find sad?" her mother asked.

"What's that, Mom?" Jennifer was enjoying some hot apple cider and she took a sip from the cup she held.

"What do you suppose would have happened to the Chad you know if he hadn't discovered how to communicate with you as a little girl? You took him out of himself, gave him someone else to think about, worry about, be concerned over. You've often mentioned how much company he was for you during those years. But what about him?"

Jennifer gave a light shiver. "I hate to think. The C. W. Cameron that we all know and hate would have been all that's left."

"Then he owes you as much gratitude as you owe him."

"Mom, gratitude doesn't come into this. Not when you love each other. Love is so much a sharing, a chance to be who you are, and accepted for who you are. I will never be able to understand how we managed to get together because neither of us has ever known anyone else with whom we could mentally communicate. The odds of our ever meeting were astronomical. And look at the age difference. He's twelve years older than I am. We could never have dated each other while either of us was growing up."

"And by the time you were grown," her mother continued, "and you went to work for him, he would have been too set in his ways to ever open up."

"He may still be, for all I know."

"Yet you're married to him."

"I know. And I'm not sorry. I'm willing to accept him as he is. It's the same as if your loved one was injured and became less than completely whole. He's the same person that you always loved."

"Yes. When your father realized that he was paralyzed, that he would never be able to walk again, he seemed to give up fighting for his life. I tried to make him understand that the important thing to me was that he would still be here with me.''

''That's the way I feel about Chad. If we have to keep our lives together totally separated, the formal boss-employee relationship at work, and whatever he's willing to give me away from the office, I'll accept that. Because I know that he will be giving everything he's capable of giving. I can't ask for more than that.''

By the time Jennifer arrived home on Sunday evening she felt pleasantly tired and truly relaxed. The visit had gone well. Sam had slain a few invisible dragons, which left him in a very benign mood, and she and her mother had grown closer than ever.

Jennifer felt blessed, even though she recognized that others might view her situation as bizarre, to say the least. She might go through life with a secret lover, while married to a cold, arrogant man in public. Sooner or later Chad had to realize that their marriage was workable because they wanted it to be. It might not be the usual arrangement that others shared, but why should it be? She and Chad were different. Hadn't she known that for years?

To be married to her invisible friend seemed to be enough of a bonus to Jennifer to accept whatever the future might bring.

A new serenity seemed to enfold Jennifer. She went to work the next week with an easy acceptance of her role in life. She kept the office running smoothly while Chad was away. Hopefully when he was back, she could find a way to keep his home life running just as smoothly.

The first thing she noticed when she walked in the door Wednesday morning was that the receptionist gave her a strange look. A very strange look.

Jennifer glanced down to see if she'd accidentally worn mismatched shoes to the office. She'd almost done that once. No. Her navy kid pumps gleamed back at her. As she walked toward her office she surreptitiously checked to see if her slip was showing. How could it? With the longer length in skirts, there was a good six-inch gap between her slip and the hem of her suit.

Shrugging, she walked into her office and stopped.

Her mail was stacked neatly on her desk, where it was always left by the receptionist. Right behind her nameplate. She did a double take.

Her nameplate read, "Jennifer C. Cameron."

Where had that come from? Glancing up she saw an ornate bouquet of red roses, which dwarfed the credenza behind her desk. After absently storing her purse she slid the card from the small white envelope attached to one of the roses and read, "Thank you for the most wonderful honeymoon a man could ever wish for. All my love, Chad."

Jennifer glanced around and saw that as many of the staff as could crowd into the area stood in front of the door to her office, watching her.

She turned around and gave them what she felt must be a very sickly smile. "Good morning, everyone."

"Good morning, Jennifer," came a chorused reply. They continued to stand there, waiting.

Now what was she supposed to do? Everyone's gaze seemed to move between the nameplate and the roses. No one said a word. She wondered if anyone was breathing, it was so quiet.

Chad, how could you do this to me!

She felt his love and amusement swirl around her, and she knew that he was paying her back for what she had said to him on the phone last week.

Where are you? she demanded.

There was no answer.

He could have had all of this done by someone else. In fact, he probably had. Although she felt sure he was wishing he was there to see her face.

"I, uh, you're probably wondering why—" She waved her hand helplessly at her new name and the flowers.

All heads bobbed in unison. What had they been doing, for crying out loud? Rehearsing?

"Yes, well, I thought that—What I mean to say is, we had felt that perhaps—After all, he's been traveling and—" She gave up. What was there to say, after all?

Folding her hands primly in front of her, Jennifer announced, "Mr. Cameron and I were married in Las Vegas two weeks ago."

Chapter Twelve

By the time Jennifer arrived home Friday evening all she wanted to do was to fall into bed, roll over and play dead.

She had not heard from her mysterious boss and so very secret lover. Which was just as well. She might have shot him. Actually, shooting was too quick and painless. Given enough time and energy, she was sure she could think of some really interesting and long-drawn-out ways to make him suffer.

Their newly announced marriage had created a minor riot at the office. "Too bad you couldn't be there to participate, my darling," she muttered to herself.

Of course everyone was shocked right down to their brightly painted toenails. And why not? There had never been a hint of romance between them. Not even a faint whiff. As a matter of fact, some of the women were embarrassed to remember going to her with complaints about him, only to recall that she had emphatically agreed with them.

And she married him anyway?

How could she explain? Jennifer saw him exactly as they saw him. He was just—most of the time—and fair—most of the time—but had never heard that justice and fairness could be tempered with mercy. More than once she had interceded on an employee's behalf.

But if she was happy, it was obvious they were happy for her. She had accepted their teasing and congratulatory comments with good grace, and tried to get some work done.

The next afternoon she had come back from lunch to discover a surprise shower, complete with cake and streamers, and gifts—all kinds of gifts, from gag to practical.

And poor dear Chad had missed out on all the excitement. Why was it she had a hunch he'd planned it that way?

What with all the added commotion in the office, Jennifer had gotten behind on her work. So she had stayed late tonight to catch up.

Chad hadn't called in during the week. Nor had he contacted her through their more intimate channel. Not that she could blame him. The man showed rare insight as to how she would react to what he had done.

She shook her head as she sank onto the side of the bed.

Well, she had survived, anyway. No doubt that by Monday something else would take precedence over the personal lives of the boss and his assistant. She hoped. In the meantime, Jennifer was going to fill the tub full of hot water and indulge in her favorite ritual of wine, music and relaxation.

By the time she got out, she was too relaxed and at peace with the world to be angry at anyone.

She wasn't really so very angry at Chad, anyway. She missed him too much to be angry. They had been married two weeks today, and for most of that two weeks they had been separated.

Face it, kiddo, you're going to have a lifetime of that sort of existence, she reminded herself. She could handle that, if she knew a few of the particulars. Was he even going to live with her, or would they continue to keep separate residences?

Obviously, he was going to acknowledge her as his wife. There was no reason to wonder about that any longer.

Jennifer was looking under the cabinet for her small saucepan to heat some soup when the doorbell rang. She glanced down at herself in dismay. Since she wasn't expecting company she was padding around the house in her flannel pajamas. The ones with the feet in them.

She had no idea who could be there. Jennifer hadn't talked to Jerry in months. It couldn't be the paper boy collecting. He'd been by the week before.

She shrugged. When all else fails, answer the door and solve the mystery of the ringing doorbell, she told herself. Somehow that seemed to take all the fun out of the game.

"Just a minute," she called as it rang again. She ran for her bathrobe, the old fuzzy one that her mother had given her several years ago. The sash had pulled a hole in the side, which she fully intended to mend one of these days, and she had spilled hot chocolate down the front, which left a lurid stain, but it was comfortable. And who was she trying to impress, anyway?

Glancing through the security peephole suddenly reminded her of one person she might want to impress. Scrambling to take the chain off, she unlocked the door and opened it.

"I wasn't sure you were home," Chad said, standing in the hallway and looking at her rather uncertainly.

He looked so tired. There were lines in his face and dark circles under his eyes and she wanted to take him in her arms and hold him for at least a century or two for starters.

"Come in," she managed to say, stepping back and waving her arm.

He stepped in and looked around. Jennifer had decorated her apartment with various pieces of furniture that she had liked. Some of them she had refinished. Some still needed work. Bright prints and silk flower arrangements gave color to the room.

She had never looked at it from another person's viewpoint. Jennifer had filled her small home with items that meant something to her, so that old rubbed shoulders with new without much rhyme nor a great deal of reason.

It was home.

She had a sudden attack of stage fright. Jennifer had no idea what sort of home Chad had grown up in, or what his home looked like now. He was getting an idea of the type of place his wife lived in. He could very well turn around and run screaming into the night.

Only he didn't.

He's probably too tired, she thought to herself. "May I take your coat?" she offered politely. He slipped it off his shoulders with a sigh.

"Sit down. Anywhere. Can I get you something to drink?"

She was babbling. This was Chad, for heaven's sake. Her Chad. She'd known him forever. More important, he had known her for the same length of time.

Chad sank down on the sofa and said, "A drink sounds fine."

"Hot? Cold? Alcoholic? Non?"

"Anything."

"Hot coffee, hot chocolate, hot apple cider—"

He glanced up at her, a look of puzzlement on his face. "You're pushing hot these days?"

"That's because it's so cold these days."

"Cold?" He looked at her with surprise. "Fifty is not considered cold."

"It is to me," she responded emphatically.

"Coffee's fine."

She put on the coffee, then went back into the living room. "I just got out of the tub. I wasn't expecting anyone. If you'll excuse me, I'll go and—"

He grinned. "You look fine the way you are. The pigtails are a nice touch. I feel as though I kidnapped and married Buffy."

She'd forgotten that she'd tied her hair back. Hastily undoing the yarn, she finger-combed her hair. "Is that what you think? That you kidnapped me?"

Chad leaned his head back on the couch and closed his eyes. "Didn't I?" he asked wearily.

Cautiously Jennifer sat down beside him. She had never seen him look so tired. Defeated, almost.

"Chad?"

"Hmm?" He didn't open his eyes.

"You don't want to be married to me, do you?" She could feel the pain of the thought going through her like a laser.

Chad opened his eyes and saw her sitting by his side. He lifted his hand and rested it against her cheek. "I want to be married to you more than anything I've ever wanted in my life," he murmured. "I'm just not sure it's the best thing for you."

Jennifer could feel her pulse racing. "Why?"

"You deserve more. I'm so much older, so set in my ways, so used to being on my own."

She leaned closer, so that her mouth was only inches from his. "None of that really matters, Chad, if you love me and want me."

He pulled her onto his lap and began to kiss her. Between each kiss he said, "I do love you...and I want you constantly. You brought sunshine into my life years ago...you are the greatest thing that ever happened to me." After a thorough, lingering kiss he added, "But I didn't give you a chance to say no."

"Why would I want to say no?" she asked, curling her arms around his neck and burying her head in his neck. "Those fantasies I was sharing with you should have given you some clue regarding my feelings about you."

She could feel him begin to relax beneath her. At least parts of him seemed to be relaxing. Then there were other parts....

Chad slid his hands into her hair and held her face still in front of him. "I missed you so much, Sunshine," he murmured.

"You did?" She was sure he could feel her heart racing.

"Very much."

"Why didn't you call?"

"I was afraid to, afraid to hear your voice. To be honest, I didn't need the distraction, if I was ever going to get finished and get back here to you." He kissed the tip of her nose. "We've got so many years to catch up on."

She nodded. "I know. There's so much I don't know about you, about your family, your friends...."

"You have been my closest friend. Always."

"But why couldn't I pick up on your thoughts the way you always have mine?"

"I wasn't sure you couldn't. I don't know. Maybe it takes practice. There were times when I purposely didn't want you to know what I was thinking. Particularly in the office. I felt as though I put up a mental shield between us, but I was never sure if it worked."

"Oh, it worked all right. I never had a clue that C. W. Cameron was Chad."

He hugged her to him, his hands sliding up and down her back. "Are you glad I'm home?"

"I certainly am." She leaned away from him slightly and announced, "I intend to kill you."

He smiled and she noticed that he didn't look quite as tired as he did when he first arrived. "How interesting," he drawled. "Hasn't anyone ever pointed out that it makes it tougher when you announce your intentions to the proposed victim?"

"Why did you send that new nameplate and the flowers?"

His smile widened into a mischievous grin. "Didn't you like them?"

"They were beautiful. But you knew what a stir they'd cause."

"But darling, I was only concerned about your reputation," he said, his expression solemn. "After you graphically depicted my sexual preferences in order to save my reputation, I didn't want anyone in the office to get the wrong idea about you. I wanted to be sure they knew that you were, indeed, a 'Sadie, Sadie, Married Lady.'"

"Ah, hah! You've seen *Funny Girl*."

"A few dozen times, probably."

"You mean you're a Streisand fan?"

"Isn't everyone?"

"Do you realize what this means?"

"What?"

"Chad! We've finally found something we have in common."

He began to kiss her under her ear. "I think we've already discovered a few others things we have in common, don't you?"

Of course he was right. They had shared memories of the past several years, even if he knew more about her than she did about him. The important thing was that he was now willing to share his life with her. He had come to her as soon as he reached town, even though he was obviously tired and in need of rest and—"Oh! Your coffee!" Jennifer slid off his lap and hurried into the kitchen.

When she came back in carrying a tray she discovered that he had taken off his suit coat, his tie and his shoes, and had rolled up his shirt sleeves to the elbow.

He looked so good sitting there on her couch. She had messed up his hair a little, running her fingers through it, but it made him look more human, and less businesslike. The sizzling gleam in his eye also added to the more human and less business look.

She sat down beside him and handed him his coffee.

He accepted it with a smile that caused her heart to skip. He took a sip and asked, "So how are things at the office?"

Obviously the office hadn't been on his mind for the past week or he would have called. Either that, or he trusted her enough to handle whatever problems might occur in his absence. In either event, she wasn't going to let him off lightly. "Funny you should ask."

"What's that supposed to mean?"

"Well, I'm not sure where to start," she said slowly, as though thinking. Tilting her head slightly she continued, "Should I tell you first about discovering that the bookkeeper has been embezzling our trust funds, or that the receptionist ran off to Australia with your best investigator, or that the fire only destroyed the outer offices?"

She had to give him credit. He made a quick recovery. For a second she thought for sure he was going to spill the coffee down his shirt. Instead, he sat up abruptly and set the cup down.

"You're kidding me," he said, staring at her intently.

She shrugged. "Of course I'm kidding you. What else?"

He leaned toward her slightly. "You mean none of that is true?"

"Weelll, I did notice the receptionist giving Bill the eye the other day. But since he's got five kids already and is old enough to be her father, I kind of doubt he's going to take her up on anything."

He shook his head, and pulled her into his arms again. With deliberate thoroughness he claimed her mouth with his own, as though he couldn't get enough of her. Finally, he pulled away slightly, breathing unsteadily. "How was I ever so lucky to discover you?"

"You know," she said with a mock serious look on her face, "Mother and I were just discussing that very thing last week." She began to smile at the expression on his face. "We've decided you're very fortunate to have found me."

"You know," he said, "I believe you and your mother might have a point there."

Once again he began to kiss her—soft, nipping kisses that caused her toes to curl inside her pajamas. He played with her bottom lip, teasing her with his teeth, then licking away any hurt with his tongue. When she felt him groan, she knew that the teasing was getting to him as much as it was her.

And yet something still bothered her.

She pushed away from him. "Chad?"

"Hmm?"

"We can't just keep doing this."

"Doing what?"

"Falling into each other's arms when you're in town and never talking."

He nodded. "Good point. What do you want to talk about?"

"I need to know—" She stopped, and couldn't seem to go on.

After a few minutes, he prompted, "What?" "What is it you need to know? That I love you?" He nuzzled her neck. "I do. To distraction. That I missed you terribly? That, too." He kissed her once more.

What, indeed, did she need to know? Didn't she know everything that was necessary, after all? He loved her. She loved him. He had sought her out as soon as he got home, not waiting to rest. Obviously he wanted to be with her. Wasn't that enough?

"Nothing, really. I know all I need to know," she acknowledged with a smile, placing her arms around his neck.

He smiled, and she thought her heart would melt. He had the sweetest, most loving smile and he used it so rarely. Whenever he did, it had a very potent effect on her. Talk about a concealed weapon. This man could be downright dangerous to a woman's peace of mind.

Chad stood up, pulling her up beside him. "I have a great idea."

"What's that?"

"Why don't you show me around your apartment?"

She looked around the small area, perplexed. "But this is it. You can see the kitchen from here. The only other thing is the bath and bedro—" She grinned. "Oh. Okay. Why don't I show you the rest of my apartment?"

He nodded. "Good idea. I've never been here before."

"I know. I was surprised you knew where I lived."

"I didn't," he admitted sheepishly. "I had to look it up in your personnel file."

She laughed and took his hand. "All right. For the grand tour I would like to point out the master bedroom suite—Don't stumble over the chair there," she added, "and the adjoining bath." The room still carried the scent of her bath oil. Turning, she said, "Was there anything else?"

"I'm afraid it's too small."

She looked at him blankly.

"For two people," he added helpfully.

"I'm not surprised. I didn't rent it for two people. Sam doesn't take up all that much room."

He glanced around the room. "Ah, yes. Sam. I've been eager to meet him. Where is he?"

She shrugged. "I forgot to mention that he's very shy with people at first. So he's hiding somewhere. As soon as he knows he's safe with you, he'll come out."

"I see. Well, another time, perhaps."

She watched him, a little uncertain of his mood. She had never been around him in this relaxed, teasing mood. Except, of course, for their weekend honeymoon. Even then, he hadn't been this lighthearted. He'd been much more intense, almost desperate with her at times.

He looked down at the knot in the sash of her robe. Absently tugging at it, he said, "I didn't imagine your place would be large enough for two." The knot fell apart and the robe fell open. He slid it off her shoulders and let it drop on the chair by the bed. "My place isn't suitable, either. I've never cared about where I lived. I spend so little time there."

Chad found the small catch of her zipper underneath the collar of her pajamas. He tugged at it and watched with interest as it followed a path between her breasts, past her navel and down until it reached the top of her thighs.

Sliding his hands along her shoulders he eased the one-piece pajamas off her shoulders and arms and the garment fell in a heap around her ankles.

Jennifer stood before him quietly while he gazed at her beauty.

He touched the tip of her breast with one finger and watched it react to him. She could tell that he was not unaffected by his own actions. She had long since given up trying to control her uneven breathing. Her body quivered with every beat of her heart.

Chad leaned down and gently touched his lips first to one breast, then the other. He looked up at her, his eyes shining with love and tenderness and desire. "So I made an appointment with a realtor tomorrow, late tomorrow, to go look at houses. Or if you'd rather check out some condominiums, that's up to you." He pulled her unresisting body against him. "I've decided that I spend entirely too much time traveling. I have two other men who could help balance that load. And if they don't want to do it, I can always hire someone else who wants to travel."

So Chad had given a great deal of thought to their new situation. She should have known. He was a man who made his living solving problems. Their living arrangements had probably been a snap for him.

Jennifer began to unfasten his shirt buttons. His touch had already started its magical work on her. She wanted to feel him against her. When he stepped back and unfastened his belt, she quickly pulled the covers back from the bed.

They wouldn't need those heavy blankets. Jennifer had a hunch she was going to be warm enough without them.

"Oh, yes, there is something else," he said, reaching into his pants pocket. Once he stepped out of them and draped them over the bed, Chad held out his hand. Lying on his palm was a gold wedding band, intricately carved and studded with diamonds. Taking her left hand, he slipped the ring onto her third finger.

Raising her hand he kissed it, then looked at her with love-filled eyes. "Thank you for marrying me, Mrs. Cameron. I'm looking forward to many happy years together with you."

She smiled and hugged him around the waist. "I have a hunch that the pleasure is going to be all mine."

Epilogue

*S*unshine?"

"Hmm?"

"You've got to help me."

"Wha's wrong?" Jennifer mumbled, still more than half asleep.

"I can't move."

She shifted lazily in bed without opening her eyes. "Why not?"

"I'm being held captive by a wild jungle animal."

"Of course you are," she agreed sleepily, and buried her head deeper into her pillow.

"Don't you care?"

"I always care about you, love."

"Aren't you going to do anything about it?"

"Tell him to move," she mumbled.

"I tried that."

"Wha' happened?"

"He licked my ear."

She smiled into her pillow. "Tha's a good sign. Means he likes you."

"What would he do if he didn't like me?"

"He would never have let you near my bed. He's a trained attack cat." She finally opened her eyes and had to bite her lip—hard—to keep from laughing.

Chad was on his stomach, his head buried in his pillow. Sam had obviously taken the wide expanse of bare back as an invitation to stretch out, which he had done. Now Sam lay sprawled on top of Chad, occasionally reaching out enough to lick Chad's exposed ear.

While Jennifer watched, Sam waved his bushy tail regally in the air.

"It's no longer your bed, Sunshine. It is now our bed. Do you think you could explain that to him? I have just as much right to be here as he does." Since Chad was facing the other way he didn't know that Jennifer was now awake and enjoying the sight of him taking up a good-size portion of her bed.

"He knows that. See how willing he is to share with you?" she pointed out with a grin.

Jennifer stretched and almost fell off the bed. Maybe they should consider purchasing a king-size one for their new home.

"No way." Those words were the first ones he had spoken that morning. The sound so startled Sam that he leaped off the bed and ran into the other room.

Jennifer moved closer to Chad's side and began to rub the wide expanse that Sam had just vacated. "What do you mean, no way?"

"No king-size bed. I like being close enough to find you without hunting all over the bed."

"I see. You may not be able to find me one of these days after you've nudged me over the edge. I'll have to end up sleeping on the couch."

He turned his head and saw her watching him, her smile gentle. "Do I really crowd you so much?" he asked, concerned.

"Well, let's face it. Neither one of us is used to sharing a bed." She paused for a moment with a look of inquiry on her face. "At least *I'm* not."

"You know damned well I'm not. I've lived practically my entire life as a monk, just because of you." He grinned. "I was always afraid of what you might be able to pick up and I didn't want to shock you, particularly when you were so much younger."

"I find that a little hard to believe, you know. Especially after that weekend in Vegas, not to mention the demonstration of your expertise these past several hours." They had gotten very little sleep the night before. Jennifer was a little surprised that she felt so marvelous this morning. She shook her head in mock concern at his relaxed position. "It's no wonder you're exhausted."

Chad turned over so that he was facing her. He slipped his hand along the nape of her neck and gently tugged. She fell against him with a breathless chuckle.

"You are a very apt student, you know," he admitted a few minutes later.

She raised her head slightly, enjoying the relaxed and contented look on his face.

"Do you really think so, Mr. Cameron? I appreciate those kind words, I really do. Does this mean I can expect my usual end-of-the-year bonus?"

Chad grabbed her and rolled over so that she was pinned to the bed. She started laughing at the look on his face. "I'm sorry, I'm sorry. It was just a joke, you know, a little fun and—"

"So you want a bonus, do you?"

His nonverbal response involved the total attention of them both for an extended period of time. Sam, peering through the doorway, was disgusted by the lack of attention he was receiving from his roommate. He stalked into the kitchen and waited by his empty food dish, feeling totally ignored.

Sam wondered if he could convince them that he deserved a friend of his own. Eyeing the door to the bedroom speculatively, he thought he might give it a try.

* * * * *

**Next month in Desire
look out for**

where you will meet six of the steamiest, most
stubborn heroes you could ever want to know,
and learn *everything* about them…

Here is a taster of Naomi Horton's
WHAT ARE FRIENDS FOR?

Chapter One

She'd been half expecting the call. But even so, the phone still managed to startle her badly when it finally rang, the sound shrill in the late-night stillness of her bedroom. Andie jerked awake and swore breathlessly, heart pounding with automatic alarm, and blinked into the darkness, wondering what in heaven's name time it was.

Late—she knew that much. He never called unless it was late. In the daylight, he was too sure of himself, too full of that male self-confidence he wore like a cloak to allow himself to be beset by doubts and questions and pain. It was only in the dark, late at night, when his demons would slip free and taunt him from the silences of his mind. And that's when he'd call her.

Andie Spencer, dragon slayer.

She smiled grimly and squinted groggily at the digital clock by her bed. Not this time, hotshot. You can just put those dragons to rest all on your own, because I am *not* coming out there tonight. Not this time. No way. Not at…oh, God, four-thirty in the morning. Groaning, she stared at the clock in disbelief. Four-thirty!

Somehow she managed to grab the receiver without knocking over the stack of books teetering on the edge of the table.

"Conn." She dropped back into the soft contours of her pillow, eyes closed, the receiver tucked against her ear.

There was a pause, then a familiar husky male chuckle. "How the hell do you do that, anyway? Know it's me, I mean."

"Who else calls me in the middle of the night?" she muttered sleepily. "You got it, didn't you? Your divorce decree."

Another pause. Longer this time. She could hear him release a tautly held breath, the sound filled with pain and regret and who knew what else.

"Yeah. Yeah, I did." His voice was soft. Rough. "How did you know?"

"I saw the envelope from your lawyer when I put the mail on your desk this morning. It had the kind of portentous weight you'd expect of a divorce decree."

He chuckled, but she could hear the effort it took. Then he sighed again and she could hear the faint sound of fingers rubbing stubbled cheeks.

She could imagine him sitting there, lights off, staring into the darkness with the thin sheets of paper in his fingers. When he'd first slit the envelope and pulled the pages out, he'd have figured it was no big deal. Would have fingered through the thick wad of documents carelessly, telling himself he didn't care, that he was over Judith anyway, had been for over a year and a half now. That he could handle it. That, hell, it was the second time, after all, so he was an old hand at it. That he was too blasé, too jaded, too damned *cool* to feel anything but impatient relief that it was finally finished.

But the pain would have been there. It ran too deep, was too complicated, for it not to hurt. Even this time. And so, much later, he'd have sat there in the vast emptiness of the big house, listening to the whisper of the air-conditioning and the sound of his own heart, alone, and would have felt the quiet and the solitude and the memories close in on him. And then, finally, he'd have reached for the phone.

She squeezed her eyes closed. She was *not* going to give in this time and traipse all the way out there to hold his hand and tell him she was sorry it hadn't worked out and that everything would be all right. Not this time. Not anymore.

"How about jumping into some clothes and coming out?" he asked quietly. "We'll pour ourselves a drink and toast old times and you can help me throw the rest of her pictures out."

"It's four-thirty in the morning, Connor," Andie said through gritted teeth. She was *not* going out there, damn it. "And you sound as though you've been toasting old times half the night already. Put the cap back on that bottle of bourbon sitting on the table beside you, toss that picture of Judith you're holding into the fire and go to bed. We'll talk in the office in the morning."

"Damn!" he laughed softly, the husky, honey-warm sound wrapping around her like a silken web. "You scare me sometimes, lady. But you're only half-right—it's a bottle of twelve-year-old Scotch on the table beside me, not bourbon."

In spite of herself, Andie had to smile. "Well, I'm glad to hear you're handling things with a little class this time, Devlin. When Liza divorced you, you got drunk on cheap wine, threw up five or six times and were hung over for three days."

"Yeah, well, I guess you get better at some things if you do them often enough," he said quietly. "God knows, I can't seem to get a handle on *staying* married, but I'm getting pretty damn good at the divorce part."

"Oh, Conn..." She could feel his despair right through the phone and fought to ignore it. She had to stop running to his side every time he called, had to quit—

"Andie?" It was just a whisper, filled with pain. "Andie, damn it, I need you."

Teeth gritted, she squeezed her eyes closed, every atom of her being resisting the sweet pull of his voice. "I have to be at work in four hours."

He laughed that low, teasing laugh he knew she couldn't resist. "Come on, Andie, don't be like that. What's your boss going to do—fire you?"

"I should be so lucky," she shot back murderously.

Another laugh, gently compelling. "Lighten up a little, Andie. I'll give you the day off. How's that?"

"And who's going to finish that report you need for your meeting with Desmond Beck tomorrow afternoon?"

Conn groaned. "Cancel the meeting. Hell, cancel *tomorrow*. I'll give myself the day off, too, and we'll go do something. How about sailing? You haven't been sailing with me in over a year."

"Get serious, Devlin," Andie drawled. "Getting a chance to buy out a major competitor like Becktron comes along once in a lifetime. That company's worth millions to someone with the brains—and the guts—to haul it back from near bankruptcy and put it on its feet. Are you trying to tell me that just the *thought* of pulling off a coup like that doesn't make your little entrepreneurial heart beat faster?"

"Okay, okay, no day off for either of us." He gave a weary sigh. "So bring your stuff over here with you and you can go in to work with me." He laughed softly. "Hell, Andie, you're not going to get much more sleep anyway."

Andie lay staring at the ceiling through the darkness, telling herself for the fiftieth time that she was absolutely *not* going to drag herself out of bed and go all the way out there. Not this time.

Not ever again, in fact. She was turning over a new leaf. Was giving the old Andrea Spencer the heave-ho and introducing a new improved version, one who was impervious to sweet-talking men with gray-green eyes and fetching smiles.

"Did it ever occur to you that I might not be alone?" She glared at the ceiling. "That I just *might* have better things to do at four-thirty in the morning than help you toast your ex-wives goodbye? I'm a normal twenty-nine-year-old single woman, Connor. I *do* have a life other than Devlin Electronics."

"We promised once we'd always be there for each other. Remember?" he murmured. "Not going to break a promise to a blood brother, are you? Not going to leave your best friend in the lurch when he needs you?"

Not even thinking, she ran her finger along her left thumb, feeling the ridge of scar tissue. Twenty years later and it was still there.

Blood brothers.

Then, realizing what she was doing—what he was doing—she slapped her open palm down onto the bed, eyes narrowing. "Damn you," she whispered furiously. "Damn you, Connor Devlin. That's not fair! I've *always* been there for you when you've needed me. All you've ever had to do was call and—"

Gotcha.

He didn't have to say anything.

Was smart enough not to.

Andie closed her eyes and blew out a long breath, swearing softly at him. A husky, warm laugh came down the line, enfolding her like a hug, and she swallowed a sigh, wondering who she'd been trying to kid, telling herself she'd be able to resist him. She never had. Not once in twenty-two years.

"An hour." She muttered ungraciously. "And put the cap on that damned Scotch, because if you're all drunk and maudlin when I get there, I swear I'll turn around and come home."

He laughed. "When was the last time you saw me maudlin, darlin'?"

"Seven years ago, when we went through this the first time," she reminded him testily. "And put on the coffee."

"Decaf?"

"High-octane." She sat up and rubbed her eyes. "You owe me for this, Devlin. Big-time!"

"Name it and its yours, darlin'," he said with a chuckle. "Love you, lady."

And the worst part of it was—that for those few moments it took him to say the words—he probably meant them.

*   *   *   *   *

Cruel Legacy

One man's untimely death deprives a wife of her husband, robs a man of his job and offers someone else the chance of a lifetime...

Suicide — the only way out for Andrew Ryecart, facing crippling debt. An end to his troubles, but for those he leaves behind the problems are just beginning, as the repercussions of this most desperate of acts reach out and touch the lives of six different people — changing them forever.

Special large-format paperback edition

OCTOBER
£8.99

W🌑RLDWIDE

SILHOUETTE
Desire

COMING NEXT MONTH

FUSION Cait London

Man of the Month

For a single dad like Quinn Donovan, abstinence was a way of life.
And he vowed that was the *only* reason why Taylor Hart had him all
hot and bothered…

LOVE POWER Susan Carroll

Liana Malone 'won' Jake Powers as her personal trainer for a month. He
intended to teach her how to relax—and he obviously had one particular
tension-relieving 'exercise' in mind…

NIGHTFIRE Barbara McCauley

Thomas Kane had been hired to protect Allison Westcott from
kidnappers. But protecting her *and* keeping his hands to himself
wasn't going to be quite as easy as he'd expected…

WHAT ARE FRIENDS FOR? Naomi Horton

All of a sudden, Connor Devlin couldn't keep his mind—or his
hands!—off Andie Spencer. But people who were 'just friends' didn't
act that way…did they?

DREAMS AND SCHEMES Merline Lovelace

When Dan Kingman was called to investigate a break-in, he never
expected to uncover a sultry spitfire like Kate O'Sullivan! But she
had plans—and they didn't include him!

HOT PROPERTY Rita Rainville

When Lucas McCall hired Megan Murphy, she claimed she could
read minds. But if she knew what he was really thinking, their
'strictly business' arrangement would surely be over for ever!

COMING NEXT MONTH FROM

▼ SILHOUETTE

Sensation

A thrilling mix of passion, adventure and drama

FIREBRAND Paula Detmer Riggs
MISS EMMALINE AND THE ARCHANGEL
Rachel Lee
TEMPTING FAITH Susan Mallery
KING OF THE CASTLE Heather Graham Pozzessere

Intrigue

*Danger, deception and desire—
new from Silhouette...*

PUSHED TO THE LIMIT Patricia Rosemoor
UNDERCOVER Jasmine Cresswell
THE LAST GOOD-NIGHT Lynn Leslie
SILENT STARLIGHT Jane Silverwood

Special Edition

Satisfying romances packed with emotion

ONE OF OUR OWN Cheryl Reavis
WHAT WILL THE CHILDREN THINK? Trisha
Alexander
THE WEDDING KNOT Pamela Toth
RODEO NIGHTS Patricia McLinn
BABY, COME BACK Erica Spindler
SEDUCED BY INNOCENCE Lucy Gordon